Forks in the road
A life in and out of the NHS

'When you come to a fork
in the road, take it.' Yogi Berra

Lord Turnberg of Cheadle
President of the Royal College of Physicians (1992–97)
Portrait by Anthony Oakshett

Leslie Turnberg

For Ralph & Zahava,
With love & much
admiration

Leslie

Forks in the road
A life in and
out of the NHS

**Royal College
of Physicians**

The Royal College of Physicians
The Royal College of Physicians plays a leading role in the delivery of high-quality patient care by setting standards of medical practice and promoting clinical excellence. We provide physicians in over 30 medical specialties with education, training and support throughout their careers. As an independent charity representing 30,000 fellows and members worldwide, we advise and work with government, patients, allied healthcare professionals and the public to improve health and healthcare.

Citation for this book: Turnberg L. *Forks in the road: a life in and out of the NHS.* London: Royal College of Physicians, 2014.

Disclaimer
This publication reflects the opinions of the author and should not be taken to represent the policy of the Royal College of Physicians unless this is specifically stated.

Copyright
All rights reserved. No part of this publication may be reproduced in any form (including photocopying or storing it in any medium by electronic means and whether or not transiently or incidentally to some other use of this publication) without the written permission of the copyright owners. Applications for the copyright owners' written permission to reproduce any part of this publication should be addressed to the publisher.

ISBN 978-1-86016-527-6

Royal College of Physicians
11 St Andrews Place
Regent's Park
London NW1 4LE

www.rcplondon.ac.uk

Registered Charity No 210508

Production editor: Urooj Asif Akhtar; Design: James Partridge
Typeset by Cambrian Typesetters, Camberley, Surrey
Printed by The Lavenham Press Ltd, Sudbury, Suffolk
Copies of this book are available to order from **www.rcplondon.ac.uk/forks-in-the-road**

Contents

Contents

Contents

Selected lectures by Leslie Turnberg

The following lectures are available on the RCP website:
www.rcplondon.ac.uk/forks-in-the-road

Jewish medical ethics, 2003
Harveian Oration, 2000
Dawson Lecture, 1998
Abstract of Croonian Lecture, 1990

For Edna …
… and Helen, Moshe, Leora, Yona, Tsofit and David.
… and Daniel.

Foreword

Medicine is a unique profession. Rooted in sometimes arcane biological science, concerned with the practical and human challenges of caring for people at critical times in their lives, requiring doctors and patients to make difficult (and sometimes agonising) decisions, it reaches beyond the laboratory and the clinic to society at large and to the political framework that both reflects and shapes our shared needs and values.

Forks in the road: a life in and out of the NHS, a personal memoir by one of the most eminent physicians of recent decades, gastroenterologist Lord Turnberg of Cheadle (Les), reflects this extraordinary scope and penetration of medicine in our individual and collective lives. There can be few autobiographies that encompass the transport of sodium ions across the wall of the gastrointestinal tract, and the challenges of treating patients with sometimes intractable diseases, setting up training programmes for junior doctors, of dealing with large numbers of independently minded academics, and persuading one's fellow peers in the House of Lords of the rightness or wrongness of a policy decision. In recounting a life of public service that has straddled clinical medicine, academe and politics, he moves seamlessly between the gastrointestinal tract and the corridors of power.

In the 60 years of his involvement with the NHS there has been constant change in the way we manage illnesses and the structure of the organisations within which we deliver medical care. Some of this has been in response to advances in our understanding of the pathology of diseases and how to treat them, and, more broadly, how best to meet the needs of patients. Unfortunately change has often been driven by individuals and governments seduced by simplistic ideas that have led to interminable 're-disorganisations' of healthcare. In some cases, as in the managerial revolution, they have been prompted by a distrust of professionals, and in others by an ideological opposition to publicly provided public services, most recently expressed in the Health and Social Care Act 2012 that has opened up the entire NHS to competition in a healthcare market.

He has lived through these changes and his is the unique testimony of an extraordinary observer of times that have been far too 'interesting' for anyone's comfort. He has been an important voice in the national conversation about healthcare – what it should encompass, how it should be delivered, how it should be provided and how those who provide it should be trained. He has always been a progressive, open to necessary and rational change. He has never been complacent about the *status quo*. But his experience as a biomedical scientist, clinician and leader of one of the largest medical schools in Europe has made him suspicious of the simple, untried and often evidence-free ideas – always described as 'reforms' as if their subject was a delinquent or staffed by delinquents – that a succession of gurus, management consultants, and politicians have been allowed to inflict on the NHS. His sceptical progressivism – evident in key chapters in this book – explains the respect that he has commanded from politicians of all parties and many individuals, including those whose views of medicine differed from his. I once heard it said of an eminent medical peer that his trouble was that 'he was a round peg in a round hole'. While it would be absurd to think of Les as a *square* peg in a round hole, he is not a round peg either: he has often been a dissenting voice. A saving scepticism has made him the outsider's insider.

For this, and many other reasons, *Forks in the road* will be of interest not only to the obvious audience of doctors, academics, NHS managers and policy-makers, and to future historians of the most important of our national institutions and one of the most laudable manifestations of civic consciousness in the post-war world, but also to many others. Les's memoir is a reminder of the values that lie behind medicine and of those who are committed to it. These values – centred ultimately on a sense of what is special about the encounter between doctor and patient – are sometimes lost, particularly in times like the present when the covenant between the professions and society is in danger of being reduced to a set of contracts delivered by sessional functionaries 'incentivised' by monetary reward. The half a dozen chapters on the problems of the NHS (an institution for which he has undimmed admiration) and the best approach to solving them should be read by everyone who wants to think beyond the headlines, the op-eds and the policy announcements.

But *Forks in the road* is more than this. It is the remarkable story of a man who, without the aid of a public school education, Oxbridge, and well-connected friends, but the support of a loving family, and a good deal of determination and passionate commitment to medicine, rose from a modest background to the very top of his profession and used his position to defend the values of that profession, though as a candid, not an uncritical, friend.

One of his strongest allies in dealing with sometimes difficult and occasionally frustrating circumstances is a wry sense of humour which shines out through the book. Try this for size (he is talking about his early research):

My project was to measure the absorption of iron in these patients and this involved feeding them with radioactively labelled iron and collecting their stools over the next few days so that I could measure the output of radioactive iron in an isotope counter. Not the most inspiring piece of research but, as it involved travelling around London collecting specimens of stool and bringing them back to the laboratory in the boot of my car, not to be sniffed at.

He also reflects on this experience:

It was hardly surprising that I showed that iron absorption was reduced after patients had had part of their stomach removed, but perhaps more importantly it showed me how not to supervise a young researcher. I was given virtually no supervision and left almost entirely to my own devices. The fact that I did get results at all is more by good luck than anything else.

He does not recommend that experience for anyone else and he put this lesson into action in his commitment to supporting young researchers as dean in Manchester, in his role as one of the founding fathers of the Academy of Medical Sciences, and more recently in the establishment of the Daniel Turnberg Fellowship in memory of his son who died tragically young in an airplane crash.

The chapter dealing with Daniel's death and how Les, his wife Edna, and his daughter and other family members managed to keep going is one of the most moving accounts of bereavement I have read – not the least because of its brevity and understatement. The fact that he and Edna have continued to live a rich life (and one that, though he does not say this, has enriched the lives of others) is a tribute to their grace and courage and love for each other. His honesty about his feelings – 'I have no confidence now, six years on, that the sense of loss will ever leave me or that I will regain an easy contentment' – will be of help to others who have been through this, possibly the worst imaginable, experience.

Many memoirs by public figures are somewhat desiccated – as if their authors had turned into their CVs. *Forks in the road,* by contrast, is a magnificent account of a life well spent at the centre of British medicine, and of its satisfactions and frustrations, of the *splendeurs et misères* of medical politics. But it is much more than this. It is the portrait of 'a man in full'.

Here, in short, is a *mensch.*

Raymond C Tallis
FMedSci FRCP FRSA

Introduction

This is the personal story of someone who grew up in the back streets of Salford but constantly surprised himself, and many others, by climbing higher in a medical career than he could ever have imagined possible. My story begins with a short account of how I got to where I did but, as I have spent most of my life in the practice of medicine and in observing the ways in which the health service has been managed, it should be no surprise that these are the focus of much of my story. During the 60 or so years that I have worked in or closely observed the National Health Service (NHS) there has rarely been a time of calm acceptance of the way that it functions as it seems to lurch from one crisis to another. Yet we have seen remarkable improvements in treatments, patient satisfaction surveys give the service high marks, and we are all living longer than ever before. So someone must be doing something right. In this book I have tried to tease out the nature of this paradox and examine where the sources of satisfaction and dissatisfaction lie.

I reflect too on how we, as doctors, can best serve the needs of our patients and the public. Having spent much time trying to educate medical students and trainee doctors, I discuss what roles we should be playing in producing a responsible and responsive medical profession.

I have had the good fortune to engage in these activities from the positions I have occupied as a physician, a professor of medicine, dean of a medical school, president of the Royal College of Physicians (RCP) and, most recently, as a Labour peer in the House of Lords where the NHS and patient care have rarely been off the agenda.

We have seen dramatic advances in the cure and treatment of previously untreatable diseases on the back of progress in the basic biosciences. It has been calculated that at least 50 per cent of our extending lifespan has been due to advances in medicine.[1] On the other hand, repeated efforts by governments to reform the structure and management of the NHS have left many who work in it holding their heads in their hands in frustration.

I have a strong sense of déjà-vu 'all over again' as I have worked and lived through innumerable reorganisations of the NHS, where each turn of the spiral brings us back to the reorganisation before last.

It is also the case that the NHS suffers from fluctuations in funding that reflect the ups and downs of the economic climate of the country – a not entirely surprising situation. Yet even in times of relative plenty, as when a recent Labour government dramatically increased NHS funding, a clamour of voices spoke of money being poured into a black hole to no obvious benefit. The voices of doom were scarcely silenced even though money did indeed talk. It said that healthcare will improve, as it did with the disappearance of waiting lists and more rapid access to general practitioner (GP) and hospital services. Of course the widely held negative but erroneous views left the next government able to curtail spending on the basis that there are more efficiency gains to be made.

Some structural changes are certainly needed. A service designed for the hospital care of acutely ill patients has mostly ignored the problems of dealing with most elderly people with multiple, long-term illnesses. We now have two distinct levels of care: high-quality services for most patients who are acutely ill, with all the modern diagnostic tools and treatments that are needed, and variable and too often abysmally poor care for elderly people with long-term illnesses. Care of mentally ill individuals is also in a dire state in many places.

Unfortunately none of a bewildering series of reforms in the last 20 years has been focused on these difficulties. Instead they have served mainly to destabilise those who work in the service as layers of administration are disbanded and reformed, and redundancy and re-employment have followed. Repeated structural changes, hardly ever on the basis of evidence, inflicted on the NHS by a succession of secretaries of state wanting to make their mark, not only pose distracting challenges to those working in the service but do nothing to correct glaring defects, especially in long-term care. It is regrettable that collective memories are short and the same mistakes seem to be made with each turn of the screw.

I am doubtful whether I will be able to convince anyone in a position of responsibility for the future of the NHS to curtail their enthusiasm for reform. But I cannot resist the temptation of warning them of the dangers.

I have tried to answer the question often posed about whether we need to continue to attract high academic achievers into our medical schools. Would we not be better off seeking characteristics that lead to a compassionate and caring profession? The question seems to be based on the presumption that high academic achievement somehow excludes a capacity for compassion. It is an idea for which I do not have much sympathy.

I spent some time as president of the Medical Protection Society when I was brought face to face with doctors who had not lived up to the standards of care that I had hoped to have instilled in my students until then. A salutary experience and I reflect here on why that might have happened and on what it means to be a doctor in today's world.

There are other questions that I try to answer. We are now in the difficult position of being unable to assess the training, skills or competence of doctors from other EU countries when they arrive to work in the UK. The rush by the Department of Health in 1995 to comply with a flawed system of mutual recognition of specialist medical training across the European Community has left us in a poor position to ensure the safety of our patients. Recently there has been some belated recognition of this problem but the repercussions of this seemingly negligent decision some years ago, although foreseen, were ignored. It was one of those rather too common occasions when I swam as strongly as I could against a tide of opposition and in which I was ultimately unsuccessful. Perhaps too, at a time when my interventions are largely forgotten, I cannot resist the temptation to say 'I told you so'.

I can describe this unhappy episode from the position I then occupied as chairman of the Specialist Training Authority – more later about that authority's establishment, and its fairly rapid dissolution.

I had a knack of setting up new bodies that seemed at the time to be absolutely essential but that failed, for one reason or another, to realise their potential. Fortunately, not all were doomed and I can take some pride, for example, in my role in the formation of the Academy of Medical Sciences in 1998.

I describe both the successes and failures of my efforts to develop new organisations in the belief that lessons, at least about what not to do, might be passed on.

I write too about a number of activities that have brought me into direct contact with government, a relationship that has not always been comfortable. Some dealings were indeed rewarding, including the review of London's health services which I was asked to lead by Labour's then new secretary of state, Frank Dobson, in 1997. Others, such as my chairmanship of the Public Health Laboratory Service, a remarkable organisation working very successfully to protect the public from outbreaks of infectious diseases, allowed me to discover a rather less attractive side of a Department of Health that appeared more obstructive than supportive of a body fulfilling such an important public role.

In recent years I have taken a strong interest in the Middle East and in Israel's relationships with its neighbours. My interventions in the Lords on these difficult and controversial affairs, along with health service matters, have been prominent foci of my activities there.

I thought that it might be worthwhile trying to explain how someone like myself came to be in a position to play the roles that I did when my background and character seem, to me at least, to be so unsuitable.

In the belief that a person's character is formed in early life I explore my own childhood in the hope that it might provide clues to my sense of identity. Fortunately for readers my memories are few and fleeting. I am, however, aware that the idea that I would rise from a deprived area of Salford to the heights of my profession would have been unthinkable only a few years ago.

Only belatedly did I begin to gain some confidence in my own views. Even now, when it is quite unfashionable, I tend to bow to authority. I am told that I hide this defect quite well but I know it is there. In childhood and early adult life I rarely felt the pull towards a clear destiny and relied heavily on the drift of circumstances to make any progress. I have always been unconvinced by the need to make plans for too far into the future, at least for myself. Paradoxically I rarely look back either and I have taken little interest in family trees or genealogy.

So, although I have always found it awkward to talk about myself and it may be out of character to find myself writing this memoir, I am prompted to do so because it does seem possible to learn something during a reasonable lifespan and I am arrogant enough to want to pass it on.

The first part of this book deals mainly with my own personal development while the remainder focuses on the work that I have done in the last few years in various guises, and my impressions of some of the important events that occurred during this time. I write too about the death of our son, Daniel, a tragedy that has dominated my thoughts during the last few years and made anything that I may have achieved seem less meaningful. I could not resist the strong urge to express my sense of loss in this story.

Leslie Turnberg
London, 2014.

Chapter 1 **Early years**

Origins

Hyman (Hymie) Turnberg, my father, was born in Iasi in Romania in 1911 of orthodox Jewish parents. Recently married, poor and under pressure from the latest wave of anti-Semitism, my grandparents took their infant son and started a new life in England. Iasi had been a place of Jewish learning for centuries and had one of the first Yiddish newspapers and Jewish theatres until the Second World War and the holocaust. Anti-Semitism was not foreign before that, however. Synagogue buildings were restricted in height and had to be built partly below ground level, and the occasional outburst of persecution made life uncomfortable for Jews.

When I came to know my grandfather in later life I recognised some of the characteristics that must have motivated him to take this precarious step, with a new wife and child, when most did not. I remember him as a short, round, jolly man with great enthusiasms and a spirit of adventure that led him to travel abroad in later life, when long trips were not without hazards.

On the journey to England they also found a new name.

Many families were known only by their forenames and my grandfather was simply Shimon Nosen ben Shimon, Simon Nathan son of Simon. He was the child of Malca and Haim Ben Shimon (Hyman the son of Simon). The surname Turnberg, however, does not appear in any of their Romanian papers. It seems to have come out of the blue as an invention at the immigration desk and it is quite unclear who did the inventing. Indeed the Turnbergs seemed also to have had an alias: Turenberg known as Turnberg. They had no surname when they left Romania but had one by the time they reached Manchester. An unusual name and, apart from my immediate family, the only other Turnbergs I have been able to discover, Catholics of Scandinavian origin, are somewhat unlikely relatives of Romanian Jews.

They eventually arrived in Manchester where they found a supportive community that helped new immigrant Jews find work and a home.

Manchester then was a centre of the clothing industry and, in a city where rain was not notably absent, of the raincoat manufacturing trade. Many immigrant Jews found themselves at the sewing machines in the innumerable factories, large and small, and it was natural that my grandfather should start work in one of those.

Their next four children arrived in short succession and, with life becoming increasingly hard, it was inevitable that my father would leave school as early as possible to help support the family. The school leaving age was 14 years but he left at 13, his true age having been undocumented when he arrived in England and advantage was taken of that to stop his schooling almost before it had begun.

This 13-year-old boy quickly became adept on a sewing machine in a raincoat factory.

It was also the case that none of his brothers and sisters was able to enter higher education, all leaving at the age of 14. Nothing of that background, however, seemed to leave them miserable. In fact they were a particularly jolly lot with a keen sense of humour. My early memories of them are as the source of a cacophony of noise with jokes and laughter. Saturday afternoons were lively affairs full of cake, tea and loud, gleeful argument.

My father's two brothers served in the army during the Second World War but he was regarded as an alien. Having not been naturalised on arrival from Romania at the age of six months and, since he had hardly been out of Manchester let alone the UK, he had never needed to apply for a passport, nor did he find a reason to correct this anomaly throughout his life. It was inevitable, if a surprise, that at the outbreak of war he should be sent to a detention centre in the Isle of Man, not only as an alien but as an enemy alien. He was treated fairly comfortably and certainly never complained.

Fortunately he was allowed home after a couple of months when it was realised that he posed little threat to national security. All was forgiven too when later he was allowed to join the ARP, the Home Guard, and issued with a helmet, flashlight and gas mask.

My mother was born in Manchester of Polish parents, both immigrants from oppression in their native villages. Her father was a shadowy figure to me because he left the marital home shortly after the birth of twins, a brother and sister to my mother. He turned up some years later in Dublin where he continued his trade as a carpenter. In the meantime, I learnt many years later, he appears to have entered a bigamous relationship, and sired more children before disappearing again. Despite all this my mother worshipped him, continuing to write to him and visit when she could, although a trip to Dublin involved a long train journey and an uncomfortable sea voyage. It was a rare and expensive experience during the war. I am saddened by the knowledge that I had the opportunity of meeting him only a couple of times as a very young child before he died at the age of 57. He certainly sounds an interesting rogue.

My grandmother, born in Poland, was a doughty individual. She had to find the means to support her growing family and rapidly developed a range of entrepreneurial skills. She set up a second-hand furniture shop and travelled the north of England buying furniture at auction in sales rooms to be sold on to the local community. I may have inherited from her my love of auctions. When her shop was badly damaged during the Second World War she rapidly restored her business and was soon back in action.

My mother took on some of her determined character and was certainly someone whom it was difficult to dissuade once she had decided on a course of action. She too had to leave school as soon as she was capable of earning any money, and was drafted into the clothing industry in a large local factory.

Love blossomed at the age of 16 across the unromantic clatter of sewing machines. My father, also aged 16, won her over by making her laugh she later admitted. They married early, aged 21, and within 10 months, in 1934, I was born.

Immediately my young parents became a pair of doting and, I later recognised, over-protective, guardians of my every moment. Each was the oldest of their siblings, all unmarried, so I was soon surrounded by a ready-made community of worshipping grandparents and teenage uncles and aunts. I was the subject of considerable cocooning by my parents who wrapped me in multiple layers of the woollen Chillproof vests then in fashion. A simple sniffle was an immediate call for some form of treatment, usually Vic rubbed into the chest and, if that did not work, Fenning's Fever Curer was brought out. This was a remarkable and potent medicine containing a dilute solution of nitric acid and I well remember its interesting taste and the effect it had on my teeth which felt as though their surfaces were being eroded, as indeed, I suppose they were.

These were the days well before antibiotics had been discovered and there was much anxiety about the possibility of catching TB.

I had a persistent and irritating cough for a number of years that caused much worry. On one occasion I was admitted to the Northern Hospital, the hospital in which I was destined to spend my first six months as a newly graduated house officer. During that admission the only observations that I can remember were my temperature and pulse rate, plus a chest X-ray. I was quite happy there but not so my parents who hovered around in anxiety until I was given the all clear.

With no knowledge of any other existence, I accepted all this attention as the norm and, in the absence of any conflict, it is little wonder that I lacked aggressive instincts as a child and later. For many years it left me with little self-confidence in the rougher world outside.

I remain to be convinced that this is an ideal introduction to any life in which competition will become an inevitable part. But my father, born into poverty and with an uncertain future in employment, was fearful that more children would pose problems. He thought that sticking at one would give me a better chance than he had had. And it worked. I was the first in my entire family to go on to higher education let alone into a profession, much to their delight and pride. I am convinced that my father, denied a formal education, would have gone on to higher things given the chance. He was certainly bright enough but was forced into a narrow life with few outlets. It was to me that he gave all the chances he never had. He was a short, gentle man who always seemed to be in a good mood. He suffered a variety of illnesses and I remember, for example, his infected ears, I presume due to otitis media. Before antibiotics, his treatment, at weekly visits to the ear, nose and throat hospital, included packing the ears with what seemed like yards of gauze strips stained with gentian violet. When he was still in his 30s he had all his teeth removed by a German dentist for gingivitis, a rather radical treatment you might think considering that his teeth themselves were healthy. He had his prostate gland removed in his 60s by what seems to me now to have been a brutal procedure in which the surgeon cored out the gland blindly with his finger inserted through an incision in the bladder. I am saddened by the knowledge that, if he had lived his life now, he would not have suffered any of these illnesses or their brutal treatments as he did then.

But I never heard him complain. He smoked heavily for many years, suffering a chronic cough ending in chronic obstructive lung disease which eventually led to his death at the age of 73. My mother lived on for another 20 years, dying of pulmonary emboli at age 94. In her latter years she became increasingly immobilised by arthritis in her knees and spine and, although her eyesight also deteriorated, her mind remained crystal clear. She spent the last few years of her life in an old people's home which she enjoyed, at least initially. She became increasingly depressed at her immobility towards the end of her life but never lost her desire to be beautifully turned out. She was always well made up, her white hair was carefully combed and, wearing one of her large range of Grazia suits, she always looked immaculate whenever I visited.

Childhood

My early memories are fleeting and my interpretation of them is limited. Psychologists might think that this failure of recall suggests that I suppressed some trauma or stress in early life, but in all honesty I cannot believe that to be the case.

I have, however, made much of the fact that I was an only child and indeed hidden behind it throughout my life. It certainly made me self-contained, introverted, self-sufficient and, I fear, somewhat selfish, particularly in my teens and early adult life.

Despite 'humble beginnings' I cannot say that I ever felt deprived nor do I think that these were drivers to any ambition I may have later developed. In fact, rather than being something to be aimed for, I have always found any achievement I may have had something of a surprise.

A 'back-to-back, two-up two-down' terraced house with a backyard and outside lavatory, typical of 1930s' Salford, was my complete world for the first nine years of my life. Momentous as the years were from 1934, when I was born, until the end of the war in 1945, I took them to be just part of a normal childhood. Although poor, these early years were never blighted by the abject grinding poverty of many in the 1930s. We were never in the position where malnutrition or inadequate clothing was in the offing. Certainly today's accepted necessities – cars, fridges, washing machines, showers and even plumbed baths – either did not exist or were beyond our reach, and fears for the future and unemployment were always round the corner. Running to the toilet in a far corner of the whitewashed backyard on a rainy winter's evening was never a joy. A large zinc bathtub was wheeled out once a week for a bath in front of the open fire in the kitchen. In the summer, food was kept cool in a simple wood-framed cabinet with wire mesh walls outside the kitchen in the backyard.

But seemingly contented parents with modest ambitions cushioned my existence. We lived in the midst of Salford with its row upon row of back-to-back terraced houses occupied by like-minded neighbours – Sussex Street, Elton Street, Gordon Street – many of which have disappeared. All neighbours were hard working and if anti-Semitism existed there I was unaware of it. This environment did not breed much envy because no one had much wealth or many possessions. In the days before television brought the outside world into the home, it was much easier to survive without envy in your own little world.

My family rarely ventured outside Salford or Manchester let alone the north west. Blackpool or Southport for holidays perhaps, but London was a foreign country. Richard Layard in his book *Happiness*[2] describes how contentedness with one's lot is dependent on where one perceives oneself to be in the hierarchy of one's own society. If everyone seems to live at a similar level, where no one has a car or an indoor toilet, then it is much easier to be satisfied with what one has. That seemed to be the case in the Salford of my childhood as it impacted on me.

At the age of six, when war broke out, I was blissfully unaware of the dangers or horrors of war. The experience of my father's internment in the Isle of Man, as an enemy alien, left few scars. He was soon back with us and volunteering for the Home Guard. He saw 'active' service on the home front during the blitzes and air raids on Manchester during the 1940s, but his keen sense of humour helped make light of these difficult years. The laughter and jokes that he brought home from his nightly tours are among my fondest memories. Going round during an air raid and encouraging people to get out to the shelters he was met by a couple slow to move. The wife said she was looking for her false teeth to which the husband yelled, 'Come on! They're dropping bombs, not bloody meat pies!'

Stories of the ability of Romanians to enter a revolving door behind you but to come out ahead were rife, but my father was a scrupulously honest man and extremely law abiding. Unlike many who were not sent away on active service he was quite incapable of making any financial gain and finished the war as poor as he went in. He never made a good businessman even in later years when times favoured the unscrupulous and business-minded.

When I was eight, I was sent away from home to avoid the bombs that were falling on Manchester and spent several weeks on a farm in the foothills of the Pennines. Glossop was only 15 or 20 miles out of town, yet it seemed a million miles away and being taken out of my cosseted existence might have been expected to lead to a little homesickness. But I do not think I felt any of that and was happy enough with this adventure on Mr and Mrs Wood's farm. Not so my parents who were consumed with anxiety about my well-being and I was brought home as soon as there was a lull in the bombing.

The sirens still sounded, however, and I remember being taken half asleep on my father's shoulders into communal air raid shelters. On one occasion we were crouched deep underground beneath Manchester's Assize Courts when a huge bomb destroyed most of the building above us. My predominant feeling was one of adventure and elation and I can only assume that my lack of awareness of the dangers that we faced was due to a foolishly poor appreciation of our perilous position coupled with a complete confidence in our ability to survive.

School years

A protected childhood at home was one thing but an only child who had never had to fight for attention was ill equipped to deal with the rough and tumble of school life.

I adjusted, of course, but generally by keeping my head down and by appeasement and non-aggression. I then always tried hard to avoid a fight and have never, subsequently, been much good at abrasive argument. I picture myself then as something of a loner, finding it hard to join groups and, although I did have several friends, none from these earliest school years lasted long. I had a strong sense of the need for self-preservation and often withdrew into myself. I tended to internalise any problems and did not let them go until I had solved them to my own satisfaction. I did not seek help from anyone and I have always subsequently tended to keep problems to myself until I have solved them. Sharing difficulties or even talking about them has never been easy for me. Despite this rather pathetic picture I do not remember being bullied at school. I must have been good at avoidance behaviour at least.

There was little remarkable about my school years. Primary school, first at St Clements in Salford and, for my last two years, at King's Road Primary School in Prestwich, revealed a boy of average ability and with no outstanding characteristics.

Similarly at Stand Grammar School I was an averagely achieving boy at an unremarkable school which itself had few redeeming features. Not long after I left, it folded and became a sixth form college for a few years and then disappeared completely.

At first I certainly did not excel academically and I was never one for physical sport. Gymnastics were particularly unappealing and even soccer and cricket were avoided when I could. A rather sadistic games master did little to encourage a greater interest of sports in me. I much preferred cross-country running, something I could do by myself and at my own pace and that must give an insight into my peculiar psyche.

I cannot say I was inspired by any of my teachers during the first few years at Stand. A chemistry teacher who had difficulty pronouncing the word 'hundreds' and spoke instead of 'onions', and forever known as 'onions', was never likely to capture the imagination of anyone vaguely interested in his subject.

But then in my final three years, in the sixth form, I became transfixed by science and in particular by biology. That was entirely due to Mr Burch.

Willy P Burch was an inspiring man full of infectious enthusiasm for botany and zoology and I was captivated. For the first time in my life I discovered myself by finding an area of knowledge in which I could be totally immersed. And I excelled. I came first in the class in my final year, gained a County Major and State Scholarship and suddenly was able to accept that I was capable of more than I had ever imagined. Willy P opened my horizons to what I might be able to achieve and I owe that transformation in my opinion of myself to him.

I was very touched, many years later, when he came unannounced to my office when I was already a professor and he had long retired. I was surprised and delighted to see him and to tell him something of the obligation I felt towards him long before, in 1952.

I knew then that I wanted a career in science but had no idea of what that might mean. There was no one in the family to whom I could turn for advice;

they were as ignorant as I was of opportunities in science. I thought of pharmacy and perhaps a future in a chemist's shop. Safe and secure enough and, in my ignorance, I thought it might entail the use of test tubes, Bunsen burners and retorts. I was soon disillusioned when I found myself serving cosmetics and toothpaste during a 'work experience' in a local chemist's shop. I did not stay long.

My aspirations were set fairly low but when a friend of mine told me he was going to apply to medical school I thought that if he could do that then so might I. So I did, even though I had little or no idea of what it might be like to be a doctor. And in fact I did not give much thought at all to what would happen if and when I might finish medical school. My aspirations were entirely taken up with trying to get in and, if I did, to becoming a medical student. My surgical colleague of later years, Miles Irving, set his mind on becoming a professor of surgery from the moment he stepped into medical school. I, on the other hand, failed even to imagine what it might be like to become a doctor.

Later in life when I interviewed students applying to medical school and asked why they wanted to have a career in medicine I realised that if anyone would have thought of asking me that question I would have been quite unable to think of an answer, other than that I liked the idea of a science-based course with a strong bias towards biology. I certainly would not have been able to give the pat response, now expected, that I wanted to help heal humanity's ills. The fact that a career in medicine turned out to be the best possible outcome for me and one that gave me enormous pleasure and interest was an incredibly lucky accident. The combination of science, the intellectual stimulation of trying to solve the nature of a patient's problems together with the ability to help someone in need is not to be found outside medicine and I am convinced that I would never have been as happy or fulfilled in any other occupation. So Willy P certainly started something in me.

Training to be a physician

I entered medical school in Manchester in1952. There was no question of my going to a university away from home. Although I had won a state scholarship we could not have afforded the expense. And in any case I was still, at the age of 17, very much a home boy.

Manchester suited me fine and the five years passed in a happy blur. Social life and girlfriends were my main foci and, although I did gain one prize, in anatomy, I did not excel. The clinical years were pleasant enough but I kept my head down and I doubt if I was noticed by any of the succession of clinicians who taught us. In any case, few if any of them live on in my memory as inspiring teachers and most taught us with only modest and variable degrees of enthusiasm. My memory of them now must mirror their recognition of me then. It was only to be expected that, when I graduated in December 1957, I was not appointed to any of the better house officer posts at the main teaching hospital.

It so happens that the first three hospitals in which I worked were all closed down not too long after I left them. I do not think that I am responsible for their demise but it does give an idea of the type of small district hospital to which I was dispatched.

The Northern Hospital, the Jewish Hospital and Ancoats Hospital in Manchester each had about 100 beds or fewer and, although such small hospitals are clearly not viable economically or otherwise, they were wonderful establishments for someone like me to find his clinical feet. I was thrown into a situation where I had to make clinical decisions with little or no supervision. Self-sufficiency being my byword I was in my element. Nowadays this degree of unsupervised clinical responsibility would be considered almost criminal and would not be countenanced but then, in a small hospital, there was no other possibility. And I thrived on it. I saw patients on my own in the clinics and made decisions about whether they should be admitted for surgery without the involvement of the consultant to whom they had been referred by their general practitioners. I did my own ward rounds and made copious notes on patients' progress and treated patients in diabetic coma and other complex medical emergencies without any supervision at all. And I clearly felt, quite foolishly, perfectly confident in so doing. I must have been doing something right when I found a surgical registrar accompanying me on one of my ward rounds to see how I managed to look after my patients so assiduously. Needless to say that sort of unsupervised work by a newly qualified doctor would not be allowed now.

It was only then, however, that I became aware of what being a doctor was all about. Suddenly my life had a purpose and I steeped myself fully in medicine. I was resident in those hospitals for the first four years and rarely ventured outside. It was deep immersion in patient care working the long hours nowadays considered illegal, yet I loved every minute.

In my first house officer post after graduation I worked for two surgeons who epitomised the two ends of a spectrum of human behaviour. At one end was a master technician whose skills at the operating table were formidable. But he had little time for his patients before or after they appeared anaesthetised in front of him. My job was to go round explaining what their operations were all about. Fortunately for him and me they all seemed to do remarkably well. The other surgeon was one of the kindest and considerate of men. He spent much time before the operations discussing in great detail everything that his patients wanted to know. After they came round from their anaesthetic he was there again explaining what had gone wrong because in truth he was not very good with a scalpel in his hand.

There were lessons here and I suppose that I knew then that, if I ever needed a surgeon, someone combining the characteristics of these two would suit me best but if I could have only one I would go for the technician every time. There were others who could offer me moral support but few trained well enough to be entrusted with my anaesthetised body. I hasten to say that I have been fortunate with the surgeons whom I have needed in later life who have all been highly skilled in managing both my body and my mind.

My experience as a house surgeon did little, however, to change my mind about my suitability for a career in surgery. It was clearly not for me.

I was reinforced in my beliefs that a medical discipline suited me better as I worked my way through my next few posts. At Ancoats Hospital I worked for three excellent physicians and I must have done something right because I was rescued from the obscurity of the peripheral hospital circuit and taken on at the main teaching hospital, the Manchester Royal Infirmary (MRI), by Professor Henry T Howat.

I had been led to believe that a career in general practice would have to be my final choice but by then I was beginning to realise that this may not have to be so. It was said in those days that hospital medicine was out of reach for Jews, and indeed there were few if any overtly Jewish consultants employed at the main teaching hospitals across the country and none at the MRI. That situation was about to change as this type of discrimination became less acceptable and I was fortunate enough to start my training as it was happening.

Not that I had any reason to disdain a future in general practice, but I was so undecided an individual that I wanted to leave my options open. And in any case I was enjoying hospital medicine more and more. I was fortunate too because, of the specialties open to me, none had much appeal over what was then 'general medicine'. Cardiologists seemed incapable of doing much for their patients; how wrong that proved to be later. But then there was little apart from six weeks' complete bed rest for patients with heart attacks, no angiography or angioplasty, and no cardiac surgery to speak of. Neurology, before the rise of neuroscience made it exciting, was largely an intellectual exercise and an art with little or no treatment for patients. Chest medicine meant TB and bronchitis while rheumatology consisted largely of untreatable osteoarthritis and rheumatoid arthritis. This, in 1958, was before the impact of steroids became felt.

All the other medical specialties were rolled up into general medicine and that suited me fine. I could specialise without commitment to any circumscribed specialty. Gastroenterology came naturally to me, first because Harry

Howat, my boss ('Happy Harry', known for his taciturnity, albeit widely respected), had a predominant interest in the subject, but also because there was so little known about the inner workings of the gut that it seemed to me that here was a subject ripe for investigation and research. And I could maintain my interest in the broader subject of general medicine.

If this sounds like I was drifting aimlessly along a career path decided by circumstances there is much truth in that. I was certainly following Yogi Berra's dictum, 'When you come to a fork in the road – take it!' I did, however, make some fortunately good choices when the fork in the road appeared.

I regret that it is no longer possible for a young doctor to take this sort of route because nowadays it is essential to make a defined career choice very early after graduation.

My own history leads me to believe that not everyone is capable of making such clear-cut decisions at this stage and a degree of flexibility is not only appropriate but highly beneficial as someone starts out in medicine. I certainly promoted this idea where I could later but the resistance was often too powerful. We are left with a system of training that is extremely rigid and one that punishes those who try to step sideways or off the ladder, as I describe later.

A gastroenterologist in Manchester and London

After I had managed to pass the MRCP examinations in 1961, I was able to continue my career in general medicine when I was appointed as a registrar at University College Hospital (UCH). This was my first foray outside the safety of Manchester and I felt my provincial origins quite acutely. I was in awe of the seeming sophistication of my fellow registrars, graduates of exotic medical schools like Bart's and St Thomas'. I soon settled down but I was often let down by the Manchester accent that I had naïvely believed did not exist. One lesson I learnt, however, was that not all is as it seems and the worldly confidence I ascribed to my fellow registrars was only skin-deep. One of them, a tall aristocratic looking Bart's man with impeccably parted hair, a stiff white collar and accent to match, became a good friend. Once we were close enough he admitted that he wished he could be more relaxed, like me with my scruffy northern ways that were, to my surprise, becoming a desirable mode of behaviour.

One year at the Whittington Hospital with an old-style general physician was followed by a year at UCH with John Stokes and Tom Prankerd as my mentors; two quite different characters. Stokes was a meticulous physician who taught me much about the need for detailed observation of every aspect of a patient. Suave, sophisticated and brilliantly talented, he seemed to suffer from a sense that he had not achieved as much as he felt he should have done, despite having been a national level squash player, a professional grade pianist and vice-president of the Royal College of Physicians. I think it rankled that he had not been right at the top as a national champion or president.

Prankerd, on the other hand, was a laid-back enthusiast, full of energy and formidably knowledgeable. He was quite unconcerned about his own position and a delight to work with. He later became dean but suffered a terrible tragedy when two of his children were killed in an ambush in Africa.

I learnt more medicine and became very much a Londoner with an increasing circle of friends. I was able to take a year out on a research fellowship with Tom Prankerd in the Department of Medicine during the time that Sir Max Rosenheim was head. A remarkably respected and admired figure, Rosenheim became president of the Royal College of Physicians about that time. He seemed a remote figure at the heights of the profession to me in my lowly position, and I had no sense that I might one day follow him. Indeed if I had any thoughts for the future they were rather more domestic – perhaps a consultant job, if I was lucky, in a district general hospital. In truth I cannot remember having many thoughts about my future beyond simply enjoying what I was doing at the time.

After my year in research, and more of that later, I spent three or four months as a registrar to a remarkable neurologist. Dr Gooddy was an old-school flamboyant man who, like many neurologists of the time, was a great showman with the tendon hammer. His diagnostic skills were huge and his sense of humour a delight. It was a pleasure and pure entertainment sitting at his feet but, although I picked up a great deal of neurology, I realised that, as I could never emulate his larger-than-life personality, neurology was not for me. The fact that we rarely did much for our patients despite a clever, accurate diagnosis did little to persuade me otherwise.

After three and a half years at UCH I returned to Manchester as a senior registrar to Dr Sam Oleesky, the first overtly Jewish individual to be appointed at the Manchester Royal Infirmary. A delightful man with great knowledge and enormous compassion for his patients, he was a delight to work for. He died in late 2013 in his 90s. I learnt more general medicine to add to my experience and by the time I had finished that job a year or so later I was a well-rounded clinician.

It is regrettable that there are so few openings now for trainees to take such a broad approach to training as the need to specialise takes a grip so early in a career.

It was almost nine years before I at last settled into my chosen specialty of gastroenterology. By then I had returned to London to work with Professor Dame Sheila Sherlock as a lecturer in hepatology, the subset of gastroenterology in liver disease.

The process by which I was appointed there contrasts strongly with the absolutely fair but rigid process operating now. Sheila Sherlock was nothing if not autocratic. My friend, Tony Tavil, a research fellow in her department, had been offered her lectureship. I had been to see her and spoke about my wish to join her team. She immediately offered me the lectureship for two years while Tony was off on a fellowship in the USA. There remained the little problem of an interview committee to agree all this. An advert was put out and Tony and I applied, as did others. Unfortunately neither of us could turn up for interview for various personal reasons. However, that minor matter did not deter a strong-willed professor from appointing both of us over the other unfortunate interviewees.

How I wished in later years that I had had such powers when I had to be seen to act with meticulously open fairness. Now, applicants' personal characteristics have to be put to one side and judgements made entirely on paper qualifications and a brief formal encounter across an interview table.

Close contact with the professor was an interesting experience. One of my roles as lecturer was to look after her private patients at another hospital a mile or so away, and she would drive me down there in her car twice a week. A rather better hepatologist than driver, she had trouble finding second gear. We jerked along with the occasional grinding noise as she tried to change gear, oblivious to the strange looks of others on the road. She often wore a tall, pointed, colourful waterproof hat and that, together with the perennial drip on the end of her nose, did little to persuade anyone watching that she was anything but a slightly deranged witch as we juddered our way along. But her team and her patients, who came from all corners of the world, worshipped her. I too felt myself extremely fortunate to work for her and look back at the time I spent with such a truly remarkable woman with considerable pleasure.

The Royal Free Hospital in Gray's Inn Road was a converted army barracks and the Department of Medicine comprised several dilapidated wooden huts placed on a series of flat roofs at the very top of the hospital. Access could only be gained via outside iron fire escapes and the professor's office was at one end of a long wooden hut where the laboratories were sited. Many a jaundiced Middle Eastern patient could be found wandering bemusedly across a windswept roof seeking the fire escape that would lead them to the presence of the world-famous professor.

But the bonhomie engendered in those huts among the international band of research fellows was something that was difficult to emulate in the spacious purpose-built laboratories that the new Royal Free in Hampstead provided in later years. That was another lesson that stood me in good stead several years later when I was given the opportunity to set up my own department as a new professor at Hope Hospital. There was no sense of deprivation when I was offered a recently vacated nurses' home that became my department and a series of nurses' bedrooms our laboratories. There is something to be said for the extra effort needed to make full use of limited space and resources and it is the bringing together of bright enthusiastic people, working closely in a happy conducive atmosphere, that makes a successful department rather than the physical surroundings.

Edna and the USA

I had met Edna in London in 1967, two or three months before I was due to spend a year on a research fellowship in Dallas, Texas. My imminent departure was a spur to a rapid proposal if I was not to lose her and fortunately for me there was an equally rapid acceptance. There was no time to think whether this was a wise move but it turned out to be the best decision I ever made. There was a hurried visit to Cologne to see Edna's parents and seek their approval, thankfully forthcoming, and then off to Dallas.

Edna followed me a month or so later and, in January 1968, we were married in Dallas County Court House by Judge Tom Naylor. His strong Texan drawl was almost unintelligible to Edna, whose English was early in its evolution, and she had to ask him to repeat his questions. We had one witness, Edna's brother, who had arrived from Chicago and the three of us went out to celebrate in downtown Dallas.

It was only 10 months later, in December, that we had a full family Jewish wedding after we had returned to England and one result of having two anniversaries is that we are unsure of which one to celebrate. It provides a wonderful excuse to forget both. But a year in Dallas was an interesting introduction to marriage.

I had arrived alone in Dallas early one morning in September 1967 and took a taxi straight from the airport to Parkland Hospital, the hospital that had achieved unfortunate international recognition in 1963 when President Kennedy had been brought there after being shot.

The hospital hosted the South Western Medical School and the morning I arrived I was shocked to see a range of very large armed guards surrounding the building. I presumed that there had been another shooting but was soon disabused of that idea when I learned that they were simply the normal car park guards patrolling the grounds. I do not think I ever got used to the close proximity of so many obvious arms.

Dallas was an interesting place to start life with my future wife. We had our own community of research fellows, many of whom came from abroad and the faculty was extremely open and friendly, although broad Texan accents and modes of behaviour took some getting used to. Someone unknown would greet you in the elevator with 'And how are you all today?' When I managed to respond with a surprised 'Well, er, I'm fine, thank you very much', they gave me a peculiar look. I only later realised that the correct Texan response was 'You bet!'

I first moved into an apartment close to the hospital, an easy walking distance. I soon recognised, however, that no one walked in Dallas. There were few sidewalks in any case and one had to walk at the side of the road close to the traffic. When a friend and I did pluck up the courage to go for a walk one evening, we were stopped by a police car. 'Where do you think you are going?', we were asked in a far from friendly tone, and were regarded with grave suspicion when we replied in our peculiar English accent, 'Nowhere actually, officer, just going for a walk'.

We did not try that too often and it became obvious that, as there was no public transport to speak of, I needed a car. I bought an old Buick from a friendly dealer who, when I came into the showroom, simply handed me the keys and told me to drive it round for a day or so and, if I liked it, I could buy it. The contrast of his behaviour with that of the Manchester car salesman when I returned to the UK could not have been more stark. I was clearly doing the Manchester man a great favour in entering his showroom and he could barely have shown less interest in me.

However, there was an interesting disparity between the trust and openness of Texans, exemplified by their propensity to leave their cars unlocked everywhere, and the very high crime rate in Dallas. Scarcely a day went by when there was not a report on the radio of yet another 'slaying', often in shopping malls frighteningly close by. It seems that if you wanted to rob anyone's car you did not have to break in, it was unlocked anyway, but you may have to kill the driver to make off with the cash. The ready availability of guns must have had something to do with it and there was certainly no appetite to ban them. 'If guns are outlawed, only outlaws will have guns' ran the bumper stickers and everyone seemed to have them.

You were not allowed to conceal a gun; it had to be revealed. Getting into someone's car was an unnerving experience as you sidled round a weapon fully revealed on your seat.

'Founded in 1957' proudly ran the sign over a shop in downtown Dallas in 1967. Everything seemed newly constructed and the apartments we lived in during our time were all built during the previous three or four years. Anything older than that had been pulled down and rebuilt. Simple, but attractive wood-framed constructions, they were put up largely as temporary structures not expected to last. In the warm, consistent weather, they were pleasantly arranged around swimming pools. Quite a change from the England I had left with its cold rains and poorly heated houses built to last for centuries.

Another contrast was the behaviour of the young men and women living in our apartment complex. In the England of the 1960s the sexual revolution was in full swing and it was far from unusual for a couple to live together in unmarried bliss, only sometimes going on to marry. In 1960s' Dallas, however, living together in an unmarried state seemed sinful and was very unusual. If they wished to co-habit most Texans married but if things did not work out then it was the norm simply to divorce. So divorce rates were high among our neighbours but none lived together in sin. Indeed several had met their next spouse at the divorce courts.

I think things changed there over the next few years but we were certainly unusual at the time in living together before we were legally married by our friendly Judge Tom Naylor. In case we were asked, we were given a large Dallas marriage certificate, with a huge Texan gold star, to prove it.

It was in the laboratory, however, where the most interesting times were had and I threw myself fully into that experience. For the first time in my career I was able to devote myself absolutely, without the distraction of clinical duties or teaching students, to full-time research, and I revelled in it. I describe the work I did there later but it was an invaluable experience.

In Dallas I was asked on a number of occasions why on earth I would want to return to the UK and to 'socialised medicine'. The grass was so much greener in the USA, why would I want to leave? I tried hard to explain how good I thought the NHS was but that hardly washed and I have to admit that I was not all that convinced myself. I knew, however, that I was missing England with all its foibles as well as my family and friends, and had to fall back on these as excuses. After a year in, what was to me, the narrow confines of Dallas I was looking forward to coming home.

More forks in the road: an academic career beckons

We returned to the UK in November 1968.

I had been offered a lectureship at the Manchester Royal Infirmary in Professor Harry Howat's department and this was a point in my career where I had to make a significant choice. There were two other possible openings for me as a budding gastroenterologist: one was an NHS consultant post in London, at the Whittington Hospital, where I had been a registrar, and the other a senior lectureship in Newcastle. Should I take the NHS or the academic route? The consultant post was certainly attractive and in London. In the end I decided that I wanted to continue with my interest in research and the opportunities opening in Manchester seemed more attractive than those in Newcastle despite the fact that the Manchester post was more junior. I do not know whether I would have been appointed to the other two posts because I did not apply for them. It turned out to be a fortunate choice, however, and within a couple of years I was promoted to a senior lectureship with consultant status.

I joined the team of Harry Howat and Ted Holmes in a reasonably large department that worked closely with the surgeons, radiologists and pathologists, a valuable system of working.

Re-entry to the UK was not straightforward, however. Harry Howat had written asking me what laboratory facilities and equipment I needed to start my research and I had replied with a long list. I arrived back a few months later to find that nothing had happened to my list and I had to start from scratch. Although this meant a frustrating delay before I could begin, it was not a disaster. It was, however, one example of several incidents that threw up the contrast with the 'can do' of Dallas. To get things moving, ordering equipment, writing grants and hiring a technician required enormous effort. There seemed to be so much inertia in the system, rather like stirring treacle, and in retrospect I began to see Dallas with a rosy glint. It was only when I returned there the following spring to deliver a couple of papers at the Association for Clinical Investigation that I was able to regain a sense of perspective and recognise the reasons why I had been so keen to come home. But how I wished I could have brought back some American ways of getting things done.

The return to Manchester allowed Edna and I to think about planning a family and almost before the thought crossed our minds Edna was pregnant. Daniel was born early in 1970 and before we knew what was happening Edna was pregnant again. Fourteen months later Helen was born and we had a complete set. Hardly family 'planning', but Daniel and Helen brought us great joy and the next few years passed in the usual evolution of children: schools, exams and visits to doctors for this or that.

Chapter 2 **Professor and dean**

Starting from scratch

In 1973 I was appointed as a professor at Manchester University's newly designated teaching hospital in Salford. I wondered whether I was being ambitious in applying and went to see Douglas Black, then professor of medicine, and asked if he thought an application from me would seem like a rather trivial pursuit. He kindly said that it would not look like that and I hoped he was not simply patting me on the head.

Manchester's medical school was expanding to become the largest in the UK and needed more hospitals and academic staff to take on the load. Hope Hospital was a large district general hospital and seemed an ideal choice. Cynics said that it was chosen to frustrate the ambitions of Salford University, Manchester's neighbour, which was toying with the idea of applying to have a medical school and Hope, in Salford, would have been their obvious choice of a teaching hospital.

I cannot remember much about the interview although I did not feel at all confident and guessed that my performance was anything but scintillating. I was asked which of the two jobs that had become vacant I would prefer, the Hope chair or that in the Department of Medicine at the Manchester Royal Infirmary (MRI). There was little choice for me because I did not want to set up a rival gastroenterology department just down the corridor from that of Harry Howat and Ted Holmes. Furthermore I had always liked the idea of starting something from scratch rather than within an established department.

I came home rather depressed and did not say a word to Edna's parents, brother and sister-in-law who were visiting at the time. I was not expecting to hear the bad news for a day or so and thought that I need not bring it up and spoil the evening then.

When the phone rang I was unprepared to hear Provash Ganguli, a colleague at the MRI, telling me that I had got the Hope job. He had met Bill Stanbury, a member of the appointments committee, in the car park and he told him in confidence of my appointment. Of course I could not believe it and asked him several times what exactly had been said. But it was true. I went back into the kitchen to tell the family the news and was so elated that I could hardly speak. They had a hard time too accepting that their Leslie was going to be a professor.

Whatever the reason for my appointment, I was the first academic at Hope Hospital, as professor of medicine, and remained the only university appointee for the next 12 months. There is much to be said for starting a department from the beginning. There is no possibility of being compared unfavourably with a predecessor and this is especially true in a newly designated teaching hospital where a professor was an unknown quantity.

It gave me the opportunity of a lifetime to be in at the beginning and to be involved in the appointment of a considerable number of academic staff – professors and lecturers. Within a very few years we had six more university departments set up in the nurses' old home, and my own department had grown to more than 30 members including research fellows and technicians as well as clinical and teaching staff.

It might be thought that this influx of a large number of young active academic clinicians and scientists would be resisted or at least resented by the existing medical staff. The reverse was the case and the NHS consultant body were delighted with the boost that teaching hospital status had given them. We were made very welcome and I felt at home at Hope.

The nurses' old home proved remarkably valuable. My office had been the matron's sitting room and my secretary and I sat on opposite sides of a large dining table with our files piled up on the sideboard. Only after a year was it converted into a conventional office with an adjoining room for my secretary. We slowly converted a series of nurses' bedrooms into laboratories (I hasten to say that the nurses were no longer in them) and they served us well for the next 20 or more years. The home became known as the Clinical Sciences Building as new academic departments moved in, but to me it was always the nurses' old home and I never felt we were deprived or frustrated by a lack of modern buildings.

After a year my surgical colleague, Miles Irving, was appointed as professor of surgery and we soon set up a joint gastroenterology service with weekly clinical meetings attended by our growing teams. Gastroenterology is a specialty that requires both physician and surgeon input for the best results and there is little doubt that our patients benefited from this joint approach.

Soon there were 30 or 40 of our joint clinical team locked in lively and often humorous debate about the best courses of action and we, and our patients, gained enormously from the fact that we were all young and enthusiastic.

I was met on my first day as a fresh-faced professor at Hope by a group of medical students who seemed almost as lost as I was. I scrambled around for some teaching space that I eventually found in a recently vacated ward and convinced a couple of patients to help with a tutorial. That first group of students seemed not to mind being taught by me as their sole tutor for that first interesting six weeks. We became quite close as we each found our feet. Soon, however, new teaching blocks were built and, as more staff were appointed, I was able to take some pride as increasing numbers of students passed through Hope. We were new to the game and, because we were so keen, our reputation among the students grew. At least for those first few exciting years we remained a popular venue for them.

It took a few years before our seminar rooms, being built alongside our Edwardian ward blocks, became available. We made do with any vacated space that we could find and, despite the many deficiencies that we struggled to fill, I cannot remember any sense of deprivation to inhibit the elation of trying to meet the challenges facing us. The advantage of starting something from scratch, of making do, without a sense of history damping our enthusiasm, far outweighed the absence of modern facilities.

It was a time of change in the health service too, with the 1973 NHS act about to make considerable changes to the original Bevan-inspired health service. As the only clinical academic in Salford I was soon appointed to the hospital board and almost immediately to the health authority that replaced it. I remained a member for several years through several iterations of the authority's name that occurred without much change in its membership or function.

I quickly learned something about politics and politicians from the local authority members. As they were virtually all from one party, Labour, they acted as a caucus with one voice on the health authority.

It was clear that they had gone through the agenda for meetings in great detail beforehand and agreed their course of action so that when we came together they presented a block vote that could hardly be denied. I did, however, have the ear of the chief executive, John Duckworth, and was able to advise him on the needs of the academic community. These were enormous as we started with none of the usual support that might be expected in a teaching hospital, for example, the hospital had one radiologist, one pathologist, and no endoscopy facilities.

The absence of teaching rooms and other accommodation for students and the lack of such facilities as, for example, a department of medical physics or medical illustration, emphasised the size of the mountain that had to be climbed. I found myself constantly lobbying for more funds from the regional and area health authorities, neither of which was sympathetic. A letter I wrote in 1974 to Sir Sydney Hamburger, the chairman of the regional health authority (RHA), exemplified the nature of our difficulties:

We have had medical students with us for 12 months and have this month taken on an increased number – some 60 students at present. We now have three major academic departments with professorial heads and are advertising for senior lecturer/consultants in several other disciplines to accept this teaching load. This accumulation of expertise is laying stress on adequate careful investigation and high standards of patient care. It is also beginning to attract to Salford patients from a wider sphere than our own domestic area. I am, for instance, seeing patients from all over the region, in particular from other hospitals, with difficult problems of diagnosis and management. Inevitably the investigation of such patients demands much greater back-up facilities in pathology and radiology. These departments are very inadequately equipped in terms of staff and technical equipment for a district general hospital even without the extra regional and teaching load. Having to accept inadequate standards is leading to an increasingly frustrated staff and poor level of patient care. I am concerned also that these inadequacies may be reflected in poorer numbers and standards of potential applicants for academic and NHS posts.

Not only is it in pathology and X-ray departments that the deficiencies are felt, but it is also in the complete absence of an intensive care unit, departments of medical physics and medical illustration and in the low levels of support for university staff with consultant contracts, e.g. secretarial and technical assistance for their clinical service commitments.

And so on for several pages.

I became a constant irritant to the NHS hierarchy with my repetitive bids for more resources. It was indeed clear that we were markedly underfunded for our new-found role as a teaching hospital, compared with those hospitals that had been established for many years. But the battle itself was surprisingly stimulating and it was only when I paused for breath after a very few years that I was able to look back and see how far we had come.

I remember a visit by the University Grants Committee (UGC) and I, as a novice in university politics, was scared stiff at meeting this austere and distinguished group of academics. My mission was to point out the lack of resources – buildings, staff and equipment – with which we were expected to start a newly designated teaching hospital. Although we had some success this was tempered by the fact that universities were undergoing one of their periods of stringency.

Nevertheless starting from a very low base meant that we tried harder and whatever we gained was felt to be a triumph to celebrate.

We were becoming increasingly successful in gaining research grants from the Medical Research Council, the Wellcome Trust and a number of other grant-making bodies. This allowed us to build up the numbers in the department quite quickly and, as many of our fellows were medically qualified, they were able to provide some support for our clinical work in addition to their research.

With Miles Irving we were able to convince the dean and the medical school hierarchy to fund more professorial departments. Professors of rheumatology, orthopaedics, chemical pathology, geriatric medicine, and accident and emergency medicine swelled our ranks over the next few years.

We were fortunate that the funding for the chair in geriatric medicine came from the RHA almost certainly because they recognised the need to enhance the clinical service and stature of geriatrics, then a rather unpopular specialty.

It did not escape our notice that these chairs were in disciplines that our well-established and dominant partners at the MRI did not consider elevated enough for their consideration. A friendly, and sometimes less friendly, rivalry existed between us and at first we were clearly regarded as their poor neighbours who could be patronised. Only when we had grown to have a critical and considerable academic mass did they wake up to the realisation that they had a rival down the road with possibly more academics than they had.

Later we were able to fund a second chair in geriatric medicine and a chair in dermatology but my biggest regret was not being able to raise funds for a chair in infectious diseases. I regarded this as an important discipline to foster at that time. I did, however, manage to find funds for a senior lecturer in this specialty and, although he was much later given a chair, an isolated academic is not an ideal way to see a discipline grow. Later still, David Anderson, a senior lecturer in endocrinology, moved across to us at Hope from the MRI and was, in due course, appointed to a personal chair.

By 1985 we had one of the biggest and most productive academic departments of gastroenterology in the UK. An increasing number of patients were coming to Hope and inevitably patients with Crohn's disease and colitis formed a large proportion of these.

It was at Hope, too, that I was able to develop my own strong research line. I describe my own ventures into research later and discuss how to supervise the research of a young novice and, more importantly, how not to do so.

Several other areas of research opened up as our team expanded. David Thompson joined us as a senior lecturer (later as a professor) and worked on the control of intestinal motility. His team made interesting observations on the way the brain controlled the muscular movement of the intestine (cerebral control of gut motility), and the role of the brain in such abnormalities as irritable bowel syndrome. Michael Marsh, a reader in the department, made fundamental observations on the defects in the intestine of patients with coeliac disease while Geoffrey Sandle, with his very elaborate technology, worked on individual ion channels, that is the minute pores in intestinal epithelial membranes that allow the passage of single atoms. He went on to a chair, in Leeds, as did another senior lecturer, Alastair Watson, this time in Liverpool. He and Wynn Rees each won the British Society of Gastroenterology research medal during their time in the department. Tony Morris, another lecturer, went on later to be given a chair in Liverpool. So the Manchester School of Gastroenterology was spreading its message quite widely. When I moved to the presidency of the RCP in 1992 David Thompson was given a chair to run the department and, later, two more chairs were awarded, to John McLaughlin and Shaheen Hamdy, working in different areas of gastrointestinal research. I was pleased that gastroenterology had put down such strong roots at Hope.

Learning research the hard way

It might be instructive to examine how I started in research and some of the lessons I learnt about how to supervise research and, more importantly, how not to do so.

As a young, newly appointed, research fellow at UCH in 1963, Tom Prankerd gave me my first introduction to a project of my own. I took a year out on a fellowship which he arranged for me so that I could look at why patients who had had a part of their stomach removed for peptic ulcers became anaemic. My project was to measure the absorption of iron in these patients and this involved feeding them with radioactively labelled iron and collecting their stools over the next few days so that I could measure the output of radioactive iron in an isotope counter. Not the most inspiring piece of research but, as it involved travelling around London collecting specimens of stool and bringing them back to the laboratory in the boot of my car, not to be sniffed at. It was hardly surprising that I showed that iron absorption was reduced after patients had had part of their stomach removed, but perhaps more importantly it showed me how not to supervise a young researcher. I was given virtually no supervision and left almost entirely to my own devices. The fact that I did get results at all is more by good luck than anything else. And I was able to produce a thesis for an MD degree from the work that admittedly involved rather more than the bare outline I have given above.

It was a similar experience to the one I had later as a lecturer with Professor Sheila Sherlock. I told her that I had an interest in iron absorption but she said, 'Barry (one of the other research fellows) is doing iron. You should go away and do something with bile salts'. I was not given any clue about how to measure them or what to measure them for.

I had to start from scratch, develop a reliable, if tedious and dangerous, method involving high concentrations of sulphuric acid for measuring them in bile, and I used this to study bile salt production in patients with cirrhosis.

Again I was very much on my own, emphasising the lesson of how not to oversee young researchers. I did manage to get results and demonstrated the differences in bile salt production in cirrhotic patients and examined some of the reasons for these changes. I appreciated the freedom that this laissez-faire attitude allowed but there was virtually no formal research training and I had to pick up what I could here and there in the lab. I would not recommend this sink-or-swim type of supervision for everyone.

It was only when I went on my research fellowship to the USA to work with John Fordtran in Dallas that I finally learnt how one oversees the research of a novice with day-to-day monitoring and discussion at each step of the way. Being taught how to perform the studies and interpret the results gave me an insight into the research process that I had hitherto lacked. It is the case that non-clinical and more basic researchers are trained more formally and start their research at a much younger age than I was when I began any serious research at age 32.

I tried hard to emulate Fordtran's training methods when I had my own team of investigators later at Hope.

Serious research at last

It was John who set me off on my own line of research into intestinal transport, that is the ways in which the lining of the intestine is able to absorb salt and water. Clearly a pretty fundamental role for it to be playing and, at the time, it was just beginning to be amenable to investigation in both whole human beings in life and isolated pieces of intestine from animals using in vitro, 'test-tube' techniques.

I was attracted to spend my year with him because, unlike most in the field, instead of using animals or isolated tissues, he was working with whole human beings as his experimental subjects. It turned out to be a fortunate choice for many reasons. He was a most likeable and engaging person with whom to work. A tall, rangy Texan, he was extremely bright, productive and full of energy so that it was hard not to be swept up in his enthusiasm. I immersed myself fully in the research and was able to complete, in a relatively short single year, a useful body of fresh information. I was fortunate enough to be able to continue that line of research over the next few years in Manchester.

My biggest contribution during the year was to describe how salt was absorbed from the small intestine. The mechanisms we came up with turned out to be very neat explanations for the ways in which sodium was absorbed in the upper part of the small intestine and how both sodium and chloride are absorbed in the ileum (lower small intestine).[3,4] The model for the ileum (Figure 1), shows sodium being absorbed in exchange for hydrogen while chloride is exchanged for bicarbonate ions.

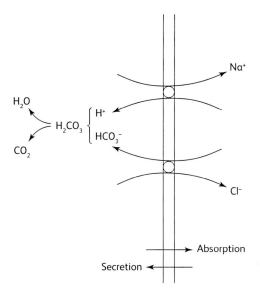

Figure 1 Double ion exchanger in the human ileum. Sodium (Na^+) and chloride (Cl^-) ions are absorbed in the lower small intestine (ileum) in exchange for hydrogen (H^+) and bicarbonate (HCO_3^-) ions. The H^+ and HCO_3^- combine to form carbonic acid which then dissociates into water (H_2O) and carbon dioxide (CO_2).

The hydrogen and bicarbonate passing across the epithelium of the gut from the body react, in the intestinal cavity, to form carbon dioxide and water. So salt (sodium chloride) is absorbed leaving a gas and water in an electrically neutral process in the cavity. I well remember the evening at home when, while analysing our data, I suddenly realised how they might best be interpreted. A eureka moment and I could hardly contain myself as I rang John late at night with my results.

Several years later others were able to confirm our demonstration of a double ion exchanger much more directly by using surface membranes derived from isolated intestinal epithelial cells. But we had shown that it was possible, despite the scepticism of more basic physiologists, to derive detailed information about electrolyte transport by perfusing the intestine of living whole humans lying on a couch.

When I returned to Manchester as a lecturer in 1968, I set up my laboratory with a grant from the Medical Research Council (MRC) and continued my studies of human intestinal transport using the same techniques that I had learned in Dallas.

After I was appointed to the chair in 1973 and moved across to Hope Hospital I had decided that I needed to develop some in vitro, that is 'test tube', methods if I wanted to gain a deeper understanding of the processes underlying what we were seeing in the whole human. I was fortunate to win a series of MRC grants and could extend my research in this way. I was happy to have Peter Isaacs working as a research fellow with me at that time and able to take advantage of his original mind. We were able to set up a method to study salt transport across isolated pieces of intestinal mucosa in small Perspex (lucite) chambers that he had designed. This was based on a method invented by a Danish physiologist, Hans Ussing, to study the ways in which frogs transported salt and water through their skin, and we simply applied it to the intestine as had a number of intestinal physiologists before us. We did most of our studies on intestine from rats but in due course we were able to modify the method to study small biopsies taken from human intestine. We later moved on to study isolated, individual, epithelial cells from the intestine, and later still to study the cell membranes of these cells. At the level of the finest detail we were able to investigate how individual ion channels in these membranes worked using micropuncture and 'patch-clamping' techniques that Geoffrey Sandle brought to us from his fellowship at Yale. Some of this work is described in the Croonian Lecture that I gave to the RCP in 1989 (see abstract of Croonian Lecture on **www.rcplondon.ac.uk/forks-in-the-road**).

This work certainly kept a series of research fellows busy and ensured that they were all able to obtain higher qualifications. We had come a long way from studying salt and water movement across the intestinal epithelium in whole living human beings.

One thing I did learn, however, was that in trying to tease out the fundamental processes underlying what we had observed in whole humans, by studying pieces of epithelium in isolation or by dissecting out individual ion channels, we came up with rather more questions than answers. Each new finding was interesting but instead of providing answers they posed new sets of questions at every step. That, I suppose, is why research is so fascinating; there is no end to the questions to be answered.

Later we worked on a number of different topics including studies of the processes by which the lining of the stomach was able to protect itself from damage by the high concentrations of acid that it produces. We described how mucus and bicarbonate are able to form a barrier and, before the discovery that peptic ulcers were caused by an infection that could be cured with a simple course of antibiotics, we thought we were on to something important as a way to treat these ulcers. That area of research, fascinating though it was in exploring some basic aspects of physiology and important for the career progression of a number of fellows, turned out to have little or no practical application in therapeutics.

It is sometimes said that clinicians should stick to looking after patients and leave the serious research to professional scientists. I, on the other hand, am not attracted to that proposition and expressed my views in a lecture I gave some time later, in 1998.

In the Tony Dawson Lecture, given at Bart's Hospital, I emphasised the point that it is essential for the future health of the population for clinicians to engage in research and focused on the theme of the clinician–scientist. This lecture (see Dawson Lecture on **www.rcplondon.ac.uk/forks-in-the-road**) expressed my views back in 1998 but much of what I said then seems appropriate today. 'Plus ça change!'

Dean of the Faculty of Medicine

It was not as if this was an eagerly sought-after job. The clinical school was based in three hospitals, south and central Manchester and Salford, and it so happens that the two previous deans had come from south and central Manchester, respectively. In 1983, it was Hope's turn. I was the senior professor there and it was virtually automatic for me to take it on. Some have 'greatness' thrust upon them and I had little choice. I was fortunate in that, much to my surprise, I began to enjoy the change to an administrative life. For someone who found attendance at committees rather tiresome I discovered that chairing meetings was much more enjoyable than just sitting as a committee member. In the chair you could at least make sure that meetings finished on time. And of course if you prepared properly, which I almost always did, you could control a meeting and finish up roughly where you hoped to be. It may seem arrogant to suggest that meetings are simply devices set up to confirm the chairman's preformed ideas but in many instances that is what they are because most of those coming to a committee meeting, at least in medicine, have not read the papers or prepared their views. I also soon realised that, if a member of the committee made some awkward point, it was much easier to open up the discussion and I usually found another member who would express disagreement so that I did not have to sully the chairman's unbiased role. Allowing a discussion to continue a little would usually allow the chairman to sum up in a way that obviated contrary views. In this way, from being a rather diffident and, I felt, retiring individual I found that I looked forward to sitting in the chair of sometimes very large meetings of academics.

For the first time I felt myself capable of performing in a very public role. And I enjoyed it. I soon realised that trying to make a large number of senior academics in the Faculty of Medicine behave as a cohesive team with a common goal was not straightforward.

In fact professors, at least in the medical school, were nothing if not individualistic. In no sense was I allowed to think that I was conducting an orchestra; it was more a case of separating warring parties. Most professors were desperate to build their own empires, to have a larger part of the curriculum, in the belief that their discipline was more important for students than anyone else's and, of course, to have more staff. Any thought of what contribution they could make to the common good of the faculty was largely secondary to their own departmental ambitions. It was the dean's job to try to weld this large group of over 100 professors into a coordinated team and it became an art to reach agreement. There was the additional competitive dimension in Manchester: the rivalry between the three teaching hospitals, the Royal Infirmary at the centre and the Hope and Withington hospitals, caused more friction than it should.

I have always been keen on making changes to the status quo and I was eager to get to grips with a number of issues facing the faculty. In particular there was the problem of the curriculum, which was clearly dysfunctional, and there was work to do on a preclinical school that was performing poorly in research.

I discuss each of these in a moment but one area where I was reluctant to see change was the way in which we admitted students to the medical school. A constant theme was the pressure to interview students for admission but I was never convinced that a short interview was an effective screening process.

Selecting future doctors

In 1986 Manchester students were not interviewed and admission criteria included an assessment of grades obtained at O levels, the headmaster or headmistress's report and the students' own views of their interests and plans. On the basis of this information we made provisional offers to those who would go on to achieve three 'As' or two 'As' and a 'B' at A-level examinations.

We were criticised for not interviewing candidates but my view was that it was extremely difficult to make a sound assessment of 17-year-olds about their suitability for a career in medicine. They are usually immature and only those showing considerable self-confidence tended to catch the eye. The numbers applying too were very large and the effort to interview all of them seemed prohibitive. But it was my sense of the futility of an exercise involving a short meeting with variably mature 17-year-olds that decided us against interview. My views were coloured by my own experience as a student when I fear I would have found it difficult to open my mouth.

I was bolstered in my belief by a growing view that there was little correlation between the later effectiveness of candidates selected for senior posts after psychometric testing, including interview, and those not so selected.

Later deans, however, were unable to resist the pressures put on us to interview applicants, although I am not aware that the types of students entering or their dropout rate has varied much since then.

In my time we did interview the more mature applicants, those who had completed a previous degree and were at an age when it was much easier to make an assessment of their reasons for wanting to do medicine. These students were often extremely motivated and had had to make sacrifices in their efforts to enter the field.

It was sometimes said that in aiming to attract only students with the highest grades we were missing out on many young men and women who were not so academically able but who had all the empathetic and caring attitudes that we need in our doctors. My usual response was that there is no evidence that high intelligence and academic ability were a bar to having such virtuous attitudes. Douglas Black wrote that 'the bedside manner is certainly an asset in practice but is not in itself a guarantee of competence'.[5] Furthermore, the medical course is extremely arduous and taxing. It is very easy to fall by the wayside if you fail to cope with the large amount of information that you have to assimilate. Sir Cecil Clothier in his 1987 Rock Carling lecture said: 'Those who propose the abolition of excellence … are fighting against an instinct to excel which is as powerful as the instinct of survival of the species'.[6]

There is also the point that a career in medicine offers a wide range of opportunities. Not everyone will have direct contact with patients. Pathologists and public health doctors do not normally have day-to-day contact whereas others, such as radiologists and anaesthetists, deal with patients but do not usually have full responsibility for their continuing care. Different branches of medicine attract men and women with different characteristics. One only has to think of the relative attractiveness of psychiatry and orthopaedic surgery, of paediatrics and neurosurgery, and of general practice and anaesthesiology to understand why they appeal to those with different characters and ambitions.

All, however, will need to be bright enough to have gone through the intellectually rigorous medical school curriculum.

I was often asked about our dropout rates. As far as I knew they were similar to other medical schools and were low at about 5 per cent. This in itself is remarkable in light of the admissions process that we adopted and the heavy load that we placed on students once they were in the school.

We were concerned, however, to know what proportion of our graduates stayed in mainstream medicine. There is a perception that medical graduates should all go into a medical career. This view contrasts with that of law graduates who go on to a wide range of occupations including many who do not deal with the law at all. A medical graduate who becomes a journalist, a writer, a musician, a politician or even a comedian, and there are examples of all these, is regarded as a dropout. I am not so convinced that those who do take a different path indicate that undergraduate medical education has failed. The numbers who do so are surprisingly small and their education is far from wasted because they bring a medical dimension to their chosen careers.

The medical curriculum and how to train doctors

I had always been struck by the fact that the young doctors I had come across several years after their graduation could not be distinguished by the medical school from which they had graduated. Three years after passing through Bart's, Oxford, Newcastle, Bristol or any other school, left few if any distinguishing characteristics in their knowledge, skills or attitudes. This seemed to suggest that despite widely varied teaching methods most of what doctors learn is from their experiences in the early years of practice. Although excellent and charismatic teachers live on in students' minds, this observation simply confirmed my belief that all we should be aiming at in an undergraduate curriculum is to instil not simply facts, but also ideas about how to use resources to gather information and develop the skills to learn for oneself – and to make the experience in medical school an enjoyable and stimulating one. These are the skills that one needs to embark on a life-long process of continuing self-education throughout a working career. How else is it possible to keep up with information that is constantly changing and accumulating at a seemingly exponential rate?

It was obvious to virtually everyone that our own curriculum was failing to meet the needs of the students. No one was happy with the way in which they were taught – not the staff and certainly not the students. Clinicians bemoaned the fact that students seemed to be ignorant of basic anatomy and physiology when they reached the wards after two or three years in the preclinical school. Students complained of the vast amount of factual information that was thrown at them in a series of formal lectures. Knowing that most of the factual information that we did manage to instil in these young minds would be out of date in a very few years did not give me a great deal of confidence that we were going about our role as educators in a rational way. It was not helped either by heads of departments who were voicing their unhappiness at the small amount of time they were given to transmit the importance of their particular specialty. Every week I was faced by some professor seeking more curricular time and, of course, more staff to do the teaching. There were also pressures from some outside the faculty seeking a place in the curriculum, for example for more teaching of ethics, communication skills, empathetic attitudes or other attributes of doctoring that were felt, by those faced with bad behaviour in our finished products, to be poorly taught.

It was clear to me that the headache of trying to put more and more facts into our programmes was not going to be resolved by anything but a thorough review of the curriculum.

I decided to set up a small committee to examine the whole issue and was fortunate in my choice of chairman, Steve Tomlinson, a young professor of medicine who was not constrained by any conservative streak or lack of ambition. I gave him carte blanche and asked him to come back with not only solutions but also a plan for how they might be implemented. As dean I was surrounded by academics full of bright ideas that they were eager to announce but rather fewer who had any interest in implementing them. If they did have an understanding of what was needed to put a proposal into action they were reluctant to get their own hands dirty.

Steve was an exception and he produced a plan that we were able to take forward despite the fact that it was extremely radical and far reaching. It involved the elimination of all formal lectures and boundaries, and a blurring of the division between the preclinical and clinical parts of the course.

This was to be achieved by the introduction of problem-oriented teaching modules with supervised small group seminars and a great deal of self-learning by the students. For example, a module on diabetes for students entering the course in their first year might entail learning about the anatomy and physiology of pancreatic islet cells and insulin secretion, the manifestations of diabetes, and hyper- and hypoglycaemia, and the long-term complications involving the eyes, feet, vascular tree and nervous system. Taught in this way most of the work was done by the students who were given ideas about sources of information, references to original work and textbooks, and from direct interaction with patients in the wards or at home. These self-learning exercises were supplemented by small group seminars with tutors who could lead discussion of the students' findings, offer guidance for further work and encourage progress through the module. The whole effort would take several weeks and was very labour intensive for the staff. The big advantage of this problem-oriented approach was the way in which it became possible to incorporate tutors from a variety of disciplines. No specialty was omitted, none could dominate and squabbles about time in the curriculum for each separate specialty became redundant.

Of course, there were teething problems and students were very hesitant at no longer being spoon-fed. Soon, however, they became more confident and mature as they took advantage of the greater opportunities and freedoms opening up for them.

It did not happen overnight. Those students who had already embarked on the old curriculum were allowed to continue under that system for whatever remained of their five-year course. Fresh entrants to the medical school, however, started under the new scheme so that for the first five years we were running two types of curriculum at the same time. Needless to say this caused logistical difficulties that required constant effort and concentration on our part.

Although this new curriculum was initiated during my deanship, its full introduction was not completed until a year or so after I had finished my three-year spell. It was gratifying that, after this prolonged pregnancy and labour, student feedback showed that the course was both enjoyable and educational. We were pleased too that it became a model for a number of other schools to emulate to a greater or lesser extent.

There was always pressure for us to spend more time teaching students about medical ethics. Although I thought that ethics should be an integral part of clinical care, and teaching should reflect this by including ethical matters during every clinical teaching session, others saw it differently. When a keen professor of general practice brought this up yet again at a faculty board meeting and pressed 'the faculty' to do something, I turned to him and to his discomfort put him in charge of a committee to look into the matter and to come back with proposals as to how we should achieve these ambitions. That kept him quiet for a few months. It also sent a message out to others pressing 'the faculty' to do this or that, that they may find themselves in charge of the exercise.

Our medical students are extremely bright and burdened with enquiring minds and we had been turning them off with our old didactic teaching methods. The release of all their creativity and inquisitiveness, by giving them more responsibility for gaining the knowledge and understanding that they needed, was a revelation. We also recognised that the undergraduate experience should be enjoyable. So encouragement, guidance to learn for oneself, and creating a stimulating and enjoyable experience were the principles on which we built the new curriculum, and it worked.

Trying to stimulate research

I tried hard to set up a system for distributing the faculty's meagre financial resources that would reflect the research activity of each department. Most of our resources went on academic staff and there was little opportunity, at least in the short term, to make rapid changes there. 'Free' moneys were, however, distributed largely on historical grounds and dependent on staff numbers. I was keen to use this money as a lever to encourage greater efforts to generate external research grant income and devised a scheme in which it would be distributed in proportion to a competitively gained grant income. I should not have been surprised by the response. Any redistribution away from some departments and towards others was always going to raise noisy resistance. This was especially the case when it became clear that the young departments at Hope Hospital were increasingly successful at gaining external grants and rather better than those at the MRI.

This arrangement was eventually introduced in a modest way but it was only several years later that a clear division of resources between teaching and research needs was put in place.

School of Biological Sciences

It had become increasingly obvious that the so-called preclinical departments were dysfunctional. They were largely made up of the traditional divisions of anatomy, physiology and pharmacology, and were regarded as subservient to the clinical part of the faculty. An influx of bright, energetic and research-active young academics highlighted the discrepancy between their forward-looking aspirations and the departmental structure under which they laboured. There was a mismatch between the burgeoning new sciences of cell and molecular biology and the straightjackets of anatomy and physiology. Excellent scientists were using new techniques to study problems that defied traditional departmental boundaries.

In teaching, too, anatomy was changing. Reliance on dissection of cadavers was being eroded as greater use was made of living anatomy, radiology and other modes of imaging.

All of this made a radical change to the structure and function of the preclinical school inevitable and Mark Richmond, then vice chancellor and himself a molecular biologist, instigated a dramatic change. He set up a committee under the chairmanship of Professor Willmot, a physicist and pro-vice-chancellor, to examine the issue. Robert Boyd, who followed me later as dean, and I represented the clinical school, with Maynard Case and Tony Trinci representing the biological scientists.

My own view was that we must release the research potential of the biological scientists by giving them greater freedom, and it soon became clear that a new school of biological sciences would have to be created. This was to be made up of scientists from the basic sciences in the Faculty of Medicine together with those with allied interests from the Faculty of Science, particularly from botany and zoology. They would have to have a distinct and separate funding stream and should be able to manage their own affairs.

We fairly rapidly reached an agreed solution along these lines and it was left to me to make the case to the Faculty of Medicine. The dangers to them were felt to reside in a potential severing of the links between the basic and clinical sciences. I argued that those links were in any case rather tenuous and it would be in the best interests of the clinical parts of the faculty to have strong, rejuvenated, research-active biological sciences with which to collaborate. There was, in the end, somewhat reluctant acceptance in the faculty. In truth, there was little option.

The result was extremely gratifying in at least one respect. The leaders of the biological sciences, Mark Ferguson, Maynard Case and Tony Trinci, rapidly developed a unity of purpose. They went in for a radical pruning exercise in which those members of staff who were not research active were purged. No excuse was allowed and they were merciless in their approach. With the savings they made they were able to appoint a cohort of high-quality young scientists and their research productivity went up in leaps and bounds. They were able to change a sleepy backwater of a traditional preclinical school into one of the leading biological science schools in the country.

There was, however, a considerable downside and one that I did not entirely predict. As the biological sciences school moved forward it threw into greater relief the relatively poorer scientific activity of the clinical part of the faculty. Furthermore, my hope that a strong biological sciences group would be an invaluable resource with which clinical scientists could collaborate was only patchily fulfilled. The basic scientists found few with whom they were attracted to work and the clinicians failed to take advantage of the potential opportunities on offer. Geographical separation was sometimes quoted as a reason for this missed opportunity but it could not disguise the strained relationship that tended to grow. Indeed more collaborations developed with clinicians based furthest away, at Hope Hospital, than locally.

The problem became increasingly significant because of the research activity exercise by which the Higher Education Funding Council for England (HEFCE), the universities' funding agency, shared out resources to universities according to judgements made about their research activity. While they were still merged with the biological sciences, clinical scientists could hide under the broader research umbrella that they provided. Once they were separated it became much clearer to which parts of the university the HEFCE-derived spoils should be distributed and clinical medicine seemed less robust than it had been under the previous arrangements.

It took some time for the clinical school to wake up and it only did so over a number of years after I had stood down as dean. I was intrigued, but extremely happy, that the medical school did relatively well in subsequent research activity exercises (RAEs). I can only presume that I had been overly critical in my private assessment of our research strength. I am sure that my membership of the RAE panels on three successive occasions had nothing to do with our ranking.

Three years at the helm of the medical school was an enjoyable experience. I gained in confidence and learned how to deal relatively diplomatically with a wide range of academics and others. I became adept at chairing committee meetings, of which there were many, and I understood the need to do my homework between meetings in order to get the best out of them. Making sure that there were sufficient numbers of committee members who were fully aware of the main issues was vitally important if business was to be completed satisfactorily: hard but important work.

It was also valuable in allowing me to meet my fellow deans from across the country and I was able to join a number of national committees. In short, my horizons were widened.

I was succeeded by my good friend Robert Boyd, a professor of child health, and he in turn was followed by Steve Tomlinson. It was important that we were all, in our own way, reforming deans and keen to see changes in the way the faculty went about its business. All of us were internal appointments and in post for a limited time of three years but there was a continuity in our ideas that was valuable.

It was only later that the practice of appointing external applicants specifically for the post of dean became the norm. There are pros and cons to both of these approaches. Internal appointments are certainly cheaper and appointees know better how their own faculty and university work. On the down side, this takes away someone from his or her own departmental activities. It may not be a good thing to take anyone away from their own research if they are particularly productive. Also, a short period of three years may be insufficient to see innovations through. As an example, the curricular changes we introduced were not completed until Steve Tomlinson's deanship some years later and we were fortunate that the three deans in office during this transition were all committed to the changes. In addition it is sometimes difficult to persuade suitable people to take the job on, leaving fewer appropriate faculty members at the helm, if only for three years.

External appointments, on the other hand, will tend to bring out applicants from a wider field and a thorough interview will be expected to lead to high-quality appointments. Problems may arise, however, if it turns out that the appointee does not perform as expected and it is then rather more difficult to get rid of him or her. Moving the person sideways may be the only option but such a person is an expensive acquisition.

Reflections on clinical practice: changes for better and for worse

I have often been asked whether I missed seeing patients whenever I moved on to something different, and when I became dean of the Faculty of Medicine in Manchester I frequently found myself defending this assumed betrayal of my vocation. I usually explained that I had not retired to do nothing but had taken on an interesting new occupation that distracted me from any sense of loss. I also pointed out that I had been seeing patients for almost 30 years and was not jumping ship too early. In any event I had imagined that I would go back to it when I finished my deanship not realising then how difficult that might be after just three years away from the bedside.

I cannot deny that I enjoyed seeing patients, many of whom became old friends after repeated visits to my outpatient clinic. The challenge of trying to make a diagnosis and deciding on the best form of treatment was always a stimulating experience and doubly so as practice was constantly changing. Practice when I qualified in 1957 was markedly different from when I became dean in 1986 and has changed even more dramatically since then. It is only when one pauses and looks back does one realise the enormity of this transformation and recognise how infinitely better off we are in our medical and surgical care. Advances in medicine must be playing a major part in the rise in our life expectancy compared with that in 1957. In the UK life expectancy at birth in 1957 was about 69.5 years and in 1989 about 75 years.[7] We had gained over five years of life expectancy since I had qualified as a doctor. If one looks at the last 114 years, improvements in mortality are even more dramatic. Life expectancy in 1900 was 47 years on average (largely influenced by high infant mortality rates); in 2012, it averaged over 80 years (for women it is 82.25 years).[7] When a careful analysis was made of the influence of medical care on mortality rates it showed that, although about 50 per cent of the improvement was due to better living conditions and public health measures, the other 50 per cent was due to advances in treatment of disease.[1]

The range of treatment options was very small in 1957 and some treatments seem now to have been more dangerous than therapeutic. I remember, in the 1950s, treating patients who had had a heart attack, in hospital, flat on their backs in bed for six weeks. It was never quite clear why 'six weeks' was chosen but during the first four weeks they were not even allowed to wash, shave or feed themselves: little wonder that mortality rates from pulmonary emboli were high. When the radical proposal was made to sit patients out of bed within a day or so after a heart attack we all stood around expecting the worst.

There were no clot-busting treatments, angiography or angioplasty, and there was certainly no possibility of coronary artery bypass surgery. Mortality rates were high and we could only dream of the good prognosis for most patients with angina that we now expect as the norm.

There were few treatments for high blood pressure and where they existed they were ineffective. We had no drug treatments for a raised blood cholesterol and ineffective treatments for heart failure, no dialysis for renal failure and little or no transplantation of kidneys or other organs. An injectable drug, mersalyl, for fluid retention was only modestly effective and I saw many patients with grossly swollen legs for whom little could be done. We used Southey's tubes, thin perforated silver tubes, that we inserted under the skin of the lower leg in an attempt to drain the surplus fluid, usually to little effect. In retrospect it resembles medicine in the developing world, yet it was the practice in England during the first few years of my career.

There were no treatments for leukaemia which, in its acute form, was uniformly fatal and few if any drugs for any of the common cancers. This contrasts with the current high rates of cure for leukaemia in children and a wide range of effective anti-cancer drugs. In my own field of gastroenterology, peptic ulceration was extremely common. In its severe form the medical treatment consisted of weeks in hospital with a constant infusion of milk dripped through a tube, placed in the stomach via the nose to try to neutralise the excess acid presumed to be the cause. If this, plus the regular use of large doses of alkali, did not work then patients were referred for surgery and the most common operation was the removal of at least two-thirds of the stomach. Later, somewhat less mutilating operations were performed to try to cut out the production of acid, but I well remember assisting at a partial gastrectomy and being appalled at the mutilation that was being performed. It was many years before effective drugs were discovered that could markedly reduce acid production in the stomach and even more years before the discovery that acid had little to do with the cause of duodenal ulcer. Then, surprise, surprise, a simple course of a relevant antibiotic eradicated the real culprit, an infection with the bacterium, *Helicobacter pylori* – no one had thought of that in 1960.

In one way medical practice was much easier. There were relatively few drugs, narrow options for treatment and, consequently, few adverse side effects. Now, there is a bewildering array of drugs increasing in number and complexity, which makes keeping up to date more and more difficult. And, as they are so powerful, they are more liable to cause unpleasant and potentially dangerous side effects.

In surgery too there were few options for many diseases other than removal of an offending organ: no transplantation of any sort, hip replacement operations were hazardous and too frequently bedevilled by infection, no knee replacements, no cochlear implants for deafness and no open heart surgery to speak of. Fibreoptics had not yet been invented so no flexible endoscopy, and percutaneous procedures via veins and arteries to inject anti-cancer drugs directly into tumours or to open blocked coronary arteries by radiologists without recourse to surgery, or indeed surgeons, were nowhere on the horizon.

So practice then was a quite different occupation from when I became dean and certainly very different from now. Patients now have an immeasurably better chance of being cured than 60 years ago; but it is of some interest that doctors were given much more respect and trust when they could do the least for their patients than now when they can do so much more. This is a topic to which I return later.

Although patients are infinitely better off with the options open for their treatment now, there were other reasons developing that made it easier for me to accept that I was about to move away from direct patient care.

The relative comfort of a doctor's life in hospital practice was about to change for the worse as I became dean. I do not think that I am one who looks back to a bygone era through rose-tinted spectacles and regrets change with the advance of time. There were, however, many aspects of hospital life that have been the victims of a 'modernisation' agenda and for which doctors and their patients are now worse off. In the 1950s, 1960s and 1970s there was a cohesiveness and team spirit among the staff in a clinical service and a pride in a hospital and its work. Many factors contributed to this bonhomie, and each was eroded slowly but surely: first, as junior doctor trainees increasingly lived out of the hospital the doctors' residency disappeared and with it the doctors' mess; few doctors remained in the hospital in the evenings unless they were on immediate call.

The consultants' dining room was withdrawn. It was regarded as being elitist so the ability to meet colleagues from other disciplines and the possibility of sharing clinical problems were lost. The ease of seeking an opinion from a colleague and asking them to see one of your patients became a much more formal and lengthy process involving written requests passing through the internal post and too often subject to inefficient delays in the system. Now it is even worse because referrals between different services within a hospital have to be approved by the primary care trust (and now the clinical commissioning groups) because they have to agree to fund the new service.

The regular, more formal meetings of the consultant staff were also slowly phased out as the managers of hospitals became suspicious of plots against them. Teams of doctors and nurses became fragmented as training requirements for junior staff increased the frequency with which they rotated into and out of a department to gain a glimpse of different services. These difficulties were exacerbated by the 'working time' directive emanating from the EU which limited the time available for trainees to train and care for patients. It soon became all but impossible to maintain any continuity of care within a department, the only remaining permanent member being the consultant. He or she rarely seemed to know which trainee doctors would be with him or her from one week to the next and the problem became compounded by the changes in nurse training. It became unusual for the nurse in charge of a ward, a sister or charge nurse, to remain for long before moving on to the next grade and away from direct patient contact and the more junior nurses, with their relatively short shifts and training needs in the university, moved on with bewildering frequency. It became unusual to meet the same nurse to accompany the consultant with his or her depleted team on a ward round and, more often than not, no nurse joined the consultant. Discovering what had been happening to the patients, whether they had had their treatment or their tests, and whether they were improving became an uphill struggle.

Contrast this sad picture with the, admittedly privileged, one that I had grown up with, in which a team of doctors, perhaps three or four trainees with a variable number of research fellows, together with the ward sister, a dietician and a ward pharmacist, would meet before a ward round to discuss each of our patients. This was a special time of great interest in which the group could come together with a common purpose to tease out the best course of action for a patient with all the facts about them available to us all. The nurses and the doctors all knew what needed to be done, and we worked as a team should. By the time I moved on I was beginning to see that each element of this system was being taken away by a combination of managerial expediency and the new arrangements for doctor and nurse training. It was these circumstances that disturbed me, made me less sorry to be moving away from the bedside and happy to leave it to my younger, more resilient, colleagues to cope with the changes. I cannot help but believe that these changes, which crept up on us, one by one, were detrimental to our patients and deeply frustrating for the staff.

Return to Hope

The experience of being dean was enjoyable and invaluable but return to my day job was more difficult. Re-entry involved taking up my clinical responsibilities on the ward, in the clinic and the usual student teaching sessions. I had been fortunate in being able to appoint a new senior lecturer to take up my duties at Hope as a bribe to my taking up the deanship. David Thompson was still in office when I returned so I could adjust how many routine duties I took on. I decided to return to the bench to do some research myself, much to the amusement and consternation of the technicians and research fellows. I did manage to spend some time myself in the laboratory, something I had not been able to do for many years before that. With considerable help I managed to do some experiments in a study I devised into the control of absorption in the intestine of rats. I cannot pretend, however, that my technical abilities were anything but poor and my admiration for the facility with which Norman Higgs, my technician, performed the experiments grew exponentially as the weeks went by. Despite my inadequacies and much to my and their surprise, we did complete the work and managed to get a paper accepted in the *American journal of physiology*,[8] one of the prime basic science journals in my field.

But it was becoming clearer that I was not in my element going back to my previous life, even though I was by then cushioned by a large team of excellent colleagues. I was increasingly restless and it was difficult to accept that I might be supernumerary to requirements. In any case I was out of sympathy with the ways in which the clinical service had to be provided, for all the reasons I described earlier.

I suspect too that many in my position who, having held larger office, have similar re-entry problems. I would certainly advise younger colleagues not to take on such roles without a great deal of caution. I would ask where will you go after the deanship?

Despite my feeling that I was not then contributing a great deal to Hope, and much to my surprise, the powers that be decided to name the newly built out-patient and investigation building after me. I am told that it was not because they had interpreted my absence as indicating that I had died and naturally I felt honoured. When I visited Hope some years later, however, it was clear that few if any of the staff or patients had any idea who 'Turnberg' of the 'Turnberg Building' was. Perhaps some long expired local mayor or benefactor?

External affairs

I had been put on a number of national committees including the medical subcommittee of the UGC, council of the British Society of Gastroenterology and several of its subcommittees, a grants committee of the MRC and, perhaps more significantly in the long run for me, council of the RCP. These and others kept me increasingly on the train to, or in, London and I appreciated the escape. I had also become quite adept by then at giving papers at meetings. I could give lectures to large medical and scientific audiences often without notes and simply using my slides. Thankfully for me PowerPoint had not yet been thought of so I did not have to prepare my slides myself. However, outside my area of competence I felt my inadequacies acutely.

I did not, therefore, believe that I could aspire to the presidency of the RCP. I was in awe of the intellectual firepower of the incumbent, Margaret Turner-Warwick, a formidable woman and the first female to be elected to the presidency. Her intelligence, determination and clear exposition of her arguments were remarkable and I knew then that I could not possibly emulate her erudition. Her predecessors too were frighteningly impressive. Bill Hoffenberg, Douglas Black, Cyril Clarke in the recent past, and Max Rosenheim and Robert Platt still in my memory, were titans whom I could not hope to follow. So my aspirations never included the possibility of my becoming president. Nevertheless there were some colleagues who, foolishly I thought, asked if I had considered this prospect.

The first indication came when a seed was planted by David Shaw, a fellow dean from Newcastle, who asked if I was thinking of becoming president. I denied it immediately and simply felt flattered. But then another colleague from Birmingham said, rather slyly I thought, that the talk I had just given at the RCP about postgraduate education sounded a little like an election address. I was embarrassed that it should have been taken that way but I found it difficult to escape the idea that had been planted.

Chapter 3 **Professional leadership**

Election to the presidency of the Royal College of Physicians

It happened quite suddenly. In 1992 Margaret Turner-Warwick had decided to retire from the presidency after only three years. Everyone was taken by surprise; her predecessors had all stayed for five or six years. The gossip started immediately. Who was going to be her successor? The number asking me if I might be interested made me wonder if I should think more seriously about it after all. My sense was that the obvious candidate was David Weatherall in Oxford: Regius professor of medicine, head of possibly the foremost research school in the UK and enormously admired and respected. He would be impossible to defeat in any election. If he were to stand then I would certainly not put my hat in the ring. I phoned to ask him what his position was. He told me categorically that he would not be the least interested in taking on such a role. He had more important things to do and in any case he was not a great admirer of the RCP. It was clear to me that his place in the grand order was secure with or without the RCP.

So my name became one of those being discussed and I was nominated by two friends, Steve Tomlinson in Manchester and Peter Richards in London, although I did not give myself much chance.

I should explain here the archaic but exciting system then in operation for election. Presidents were elected for one year at a time and could stand for re-election each year. Few if any stood against the incumbent and they could stay in post for several years. In the distant past presidents remained in office for very many years when the responsibilities were relatively light and they could continue their London practice (they were all Londoners) and run the RCP in their spare time. More recently, however, the norm had been five or six years and the duties had become increasingly full time. Until, that is, Margaret decided that three years was enough for her.

One of the important rules of the game was that candidates were not allowed to canvas for themselves. This did not prevent one's friends and colleagues from extolling one's virtues. In my case Steve Tomlinson and Peter Richards were busily putting it about that I was the man for the job, all in the best possible taste of course and without any input from me.

It was the electoral process that provided the most fun, however. Only those fellows attending the College on the day of election were allowed to vote. All who did so were rewarded with a newly minted florin, more recently a 10-pence piece.

Each fellow present wrote the name of their favoured candidate on a small piece of paper. These were collected in silver urns by council members passing along the rows of assembled fellows. The vice-president then read out the name on each piece of paper plucked from the urns and the number of votes for each candidate was recorded. Many fellows joined in the entertainment by recording the votes themselves as they were read out.

As there was rarely a candidate who had polled more than 50 per cent of the votes in the first round, a second round was held for the two who garnered the most votes. Another session of voting followed with names being read out yet again. This whole process could take several hours and was agony for the candidates but entertaining for everyone else.

When I was proposed there were five other candidates: Keith Peters (Regius professor of medicine in Cambridge), Robert Cohen (professor of medicine at the London Hospital and vice-president of the RCP), Jack Howell (professor of medicine at Southampton), Roger Williams (professor of hepatology at King's College) and John Swales (professor of medicine in Leicester). Keith Peters was, to my mind at least, the favoured candidate. He was certainly the best known and had the highest profile. Although I was reasonably well known in academic circles, I was something of an unknown quantity among the fellowship, something that Steve and Peter had been busily trying to correct. Keith had turned round the Cambridge Clinical School from being a rather sleepy downbeat place into one of the most research-active schools in the country in the space of very few years, partly by strongly linking it to the Laboratory of Molecular Biology with its galaxy of Nobel laureates, and partly by making a number of inspired appointments.

I expected him to receive the most votes in the first round but felt that I had a chance if I came second and was allowed to go forward to the second round, which is, in fact, what happened. He gained most votes and I came second. In the next round each of us would pick up votes from the unsuccessful candidates and I gained a large majority of those. The reasons are interesting. Although I cannot be sure, I felt that there was a bias against any Cambridge candidate and in favour of a relative unknown from the provinces. It was said that a large number of supporters coming down from Manchester had swung the vote. A coach-full had driven down for the day's fun but they only made up about 30 individuals and my majority was considerably larger at over 200. They were never going to make a large impact among the 750 or so fellows voting. Indeed most of those there on the day must have come from the south east, relatively fewer from further afield being willing to take the whole day off. The fact that Keith was so well known may have counted against him, too, my relative anonymity acting in my favour on the day.

As our names were repeatedly read out like a hypnotising mantra I could see them being ticked off by a colleague sitting next to me. As I realised that I was drawing ahead I began to feel light-headed and a little unwell. I no longer dared look over my neighbour's shoulder at his chart and started to sweat. What if I won? What if I became president? Until that moment I had not allowed myself to think about being successful for fear of jinxing the whole thing. Suddenly it was becoming a reality.

A few days before election day, I knew that my surgical colleague at Hope Hospital, Miles Irving, a council member of the Royal College of Surgeons, was also going through an election for the presidency of his college. Unlike me, he was widely considered to be the favourite. Elections in his college involved only members of council and not the whole fellowship, so, theoretically, were somewhat more predictable. My feelings then were that he would be elected, something he richly deserved, but I would not be. When he failed three days before the physicians' election I thought that it was all up for the two of us from Hope and that neither of us would be successful. That was the thought with which I went into election day, so when I was eventually elected I was completely bowled over.

I was led by Margaret Turner-Warwick to stand in front of a cheering throng of fellows and thence to sit in the president's chair with the gown around my shoulders. It was fortunate for me that she had instituted a change in the period of grace between election and taking up office. Until then it had been the case that the elected president started the job that evening. I, on the other hand, was given three months to gather my wits.

Edna had come with me to London but was not allowed anywhere near the RCP for fear of contaminating the election. I learnt later that she had wandered round Regent's Park with a friend all afternoon. I saw her only when she put her head round the door of the president's office after I had been elected. I had been taken there by Margaret so I could phone my mother who had somewhat mixed feelings because she knew that this would take me further away from Manchester again. Edna was also apprehensive about what it would mean for her. I had played down the possibility that I might be elected, but now she and I could no longer hide from the reality that we would be moving from the safety of our comfortable existence in Manchester to a potentially disturbing future in London. But for the moment we were elated.

The fellows' dinner followed and Edna and I were sat at the top table next to the president. We discovered that, although the unsuccessful candidates were invited, their wives were not. Edna was shocked and vowed to change that when we were in office. And she did.

Three months later I was in office. Not the first Jewish president but the first practising Jew. Max Rosenheim and Bill Hoffenberg were Jewish by birth but not in practice. Certainly I was the only one to place a mezuzah, a small prayer scroll, on the doorframe of our flat in the RCP. It is traditional to leave mezuzot (plural of mezuzah) on homes if they are taken over by another Jew. Strangely this turned out to be the case when I was succeeded by George Alberti some five years later. He had started life as a Jew but had been baptised by his parents when still a child. Having lived a Christian existence for most of his life, he reconverted to Judaism when he met and married Stephanie Amiel, a fellow professor of diabetes. So he was entitled to inherit my mezuzah.

Challenges and opportunities

The presidency was a full-time job. Living in a flat over the shop meant that I was rarely away from the office. My day often began with breakfast meetings, continuing with appointments and meetings throughout the day and, more often than not, finishing with a dinner at which I was expected to give a speech. I relished the busy life in which there was rarely a quiet or dull moment. I cannot say that I enjoyed making speeches but as time went on I relaxed into the rhythm. I told few jokes but I made considerable use of quotations and did introduce what humour I could into my speeches.

There were, however, more pressing matters than making speeches. Within the RCP I was instrumental in setting up the patient liaison committee and the regional offices of the RCP, arranging for the extension to the RCP building and the ultimately unsuccessful attempt to retain paediatricians within the ambit of our College. Each deserves some mention here.

Involving patients

I was keen to see if we could form a closer relationship between the RCP and patients. We certainly needed to take account of what they thought when we were developing our policies and strategy. But where do you find representative patients? I approached the Patients' Association for advice about the possible membership of a liaison group and they solved our problem by nominating a number of people whom they thought might be helpful. I decided that I should chair the committee to demonstrate the seriousness with which we should take the patient view. Agendas were drawn up by both the RCP and the patient groups, and I believe that the committee formed a valuable source of advice that was fed into council, via its minutes always being on council's agenda and me chairing both bodies. Some years later, after I had demitted office, the RCP went a number of important steps further when they found a place for patients as full members of council and an even greater use was made of their views.

Patients and doctors

It was inevitable that during my time in the RCP presidency I should devote much thought to its roles in particular and doctors' roles in general. My Harveian Oration to the RCP in 2000, available on the RCP website (www.rcplondon.ac.uk/forks-in-the-road), outlined some of my philosophy. One area of particular interest to me was the relationship between doctors and patients, and it became a recurrent theme in my speeches and lectures. I wrote about the potential conflict between the doctor's desire to do good (beneficence) and the patient's need for autonomy:

> *Until relatively recent years the doctor's desire to do good was heavily tinged with paternalism. Most doctors and patients were happy with the proposition that the doctors knew best what was good for patients and they made recommendations that patients tended to accept without question. The doctor believed he was acting in the patient's best interest (what Osler called a singular beneficence) and patients accepted that the doctor was acting in good faith on their behalf. However, in the last few decades, this type of behaviour for doctor and patient has become increasingly untenable as patient autonomy has increased and doctors can no longer act as gods.*
>
> *While patients trusted their doctors, the intensely personal relationship between them was sustained. But the displacement of this trust by patient autonomy has potential dangers. Trust may be lost if a reasonable balance is not maintained between these two legitimate propositions, patients' autonomy and the doctors' desire to do their best for their patients according to his or her knowledge, expertise and understanding. Just as the dominance of paternalism is unacceptable so the dominance of autonomy can be counter-productive.*
>
> *The development of an individual's right to determine his or her own medical care evolved from their rights against the state. It developed as democracy emerged over the years but it is only in the last few decades that it has evolved quite rapidly in patients in relation to their care.*
>
> *It is not a uniform phenomenon however and each patient differs in the expression of their need for autonomy. Many want to know all the facts. They want to know how a diagnosis is reached, what the chances are that the diagnosis is right or wrong, what options there are for treatment, what the likely*

side effects are and what the prognosis of their condition is. They also wish to know more about the doctor's record in treating conditions similar to their own. Other patients are not at all interested in such matters and are more concerned with the desire to be cured without bothering with the details. They are more comfortable with giving over responsibility to someone else. For some, this is more comforting, particularly if they do not have to make too many decisions that could keep them awake at night.

Complete independence is impossible and once a person becomes ill the need for detailed information diminishes. The sicker they become, paradoxically, the less they are likely to want to become involved in the pros and cons of their treatment. Nor are surrogates and patient advocates necessarily in a good position to speak for patients. They are not the patient, have their own inbuilt prejudices and cannot displace the patient's own individual autonomy. Furthermore, their assessment of the doctor's advice may come between the patient and the doctor. Individuals taking on such a role have particular responsibility that should be used with caution.

Of course, patients are vulnerable to deception. Doctors can choose or select the data to present to patients and so bias decisions patients take 'autonomously'. It is clearly the doctor's role to assist the patient to reach an authentically autonomous decision that the doctor truly believes is in the patient's best interest. None of this, of course, obviates the patient's autonomy but it does depend to this extent on the doctor's beneficence.

A physician too has a need for autonomy. After all he or she is an individual with rights. The physician's conscience cannot be overridden by the patient's will. The patient's autonomy cannot come between the doctor's need to exercise his or her professional judgement in the best interests of patients. In trying to practise good medicine, the physician has to have his or her own autonomy. While patients have the right to refuse treatment and to participate in their own management, they do not have the right to demand treatment against the physician's opinion of what is right for that patient.

There is another way in which the doctor's autonomy is important. Some, for example, may have a legitimate moral objection to practising abortion. Even though the patients themselves may be desirous the doctor is not obliged to undertake such procedures. The patient's demands for treatment may violate the doctor's own autonomy and reduce his professional independence.

Cutting across the critical relationship between doctor and patient is the action of the State in providing health services. Increasingly, there are the managerial demands for doctors to behave in certain ways and this may cut across both the doctor's and the patient's autonomy. A new generation of chief executives and managers taking a keen interest in the behaviour of doctors and taking an analytic look at the costs of care are increasingly having an influence that impinges on doctors' responsibilities. The development of rationing in healthcare and the evolution of priorities for society as a whole inevitably cut across patients' autonomy. They are deprived of the complete freedom to make decisions about their care in a system that operates universally and where there is a gap between what can be done and what can be afforded. There is no novelty in this but the recent rise of aggressive, critical, cost-conscious management intruding into the doctor–patient relationship, adds a further distorting factor to the question of autonomy.

At the end of the day, patients and doctors have to trust each other. In its absence, care is damaged and the therapeutic relationship broken.

I was far from alone in discussing the nature of these interesting and important relationships between doctors and patients and certainly not the first.[9]

Trust

There is a strong trend in popular opinion away from the unquestioning trust that characterised the average man in the British street in the years before the Second World War. Leading public figures, governments and professionals have since been repeatedly shown to be untrustworthy and now even the banks, long thought to be bastions of rectitude, are seen to be untrustworthy or even fraudulent.

It should not be surprising to find that doctors too are regarded with suspicion, at least by the media, despite the contrary view gleaned from repeated polls of public opinion.

I remember seeing a patient many years ago, a little old lady in the ward, sitting up in bed with a new hearing aid in her ear. I asked her, 'Are you hearing better?' and she replied, 'What's that, doctor?' So I said, 'You're hearing better?' 'Oh am I doctor? Thank you very much.'

I am afraid that nowadays we cannot rely on patients having that sort of absolute trust that the doctor is always right. It is said that betrayal is rampant, so the answer is ever-increasing control, accountability and regulation, to say nothing of monitoring and surveillance. You might think that with all these preventive measures everyone could relax and begin to trust again. But all the evidence is that, the more transparency there is, the more regulations are introduced and the more suspicious we become; this all costs vast amounts of money and time and is an enormous distraction. Yet at the end of the day you do just have to trust; life without trust becomes impossible. Niklas Luhrmann said, 'A complete absence of trust would prevent anyone ever getting up in the morning'.[10] And trust can never be guaranteed; in any event, where there is a guarantee, trust becomes redundant.

It has to be asked what is this doing to the patient–doctor relationship and what should we in the medical profession be doing in the face of this apparent decline in public confidence. It is unfortunately the case that not all doctors are beyond reproach but the question is whether an untrustworthy activity is really the tip of an iceberg or just an occasional aberration. And, if it is the former, how best should it be dealt with? Blanket, overwhelming, control efforts or more carefully defined regulation? The Department of Health also sends out a constant stream of guidance to practice under the overall banner of 'clinical governance' and this is coupled with managerial targets. Control and monitoring systems have multiplied in a very costly way but are, unfortunately, largely ineffective in reducing mistrust.

Yet we do seem to survive and that is at least partly due to the innate good sense of most 'normal' people who get on with their 'normal' lives happily, placing reasonable amounts of trust in those with whom they have to deal. That trust is respected for the vast majority of time and this allows us to lead a rather more contented life than that led by those of a suspicious, mistrustful cast of mind, despite an occasional disappointment.

It is indeed, fortunately, the case that whenever there is a poll of public opinion of whom the public trust, doctors come top. A Mori poll conducted in 1999, that is shortly after the trial of Dr Shipman, a GP who murdered a large number of his patients, when you might expect at least a hint of mistrust, revealed that 91 per cent of the public trusted their doctors to tell the truth; this is ahead of judges, who were trusted by only 77 per cent. This is in stark contrast to journalists, with only 15 per cent of the public trusting them to tell the truth, closely followed by politicians, with only 23 per cent of the population agreeing that they told the truth.

As far as doctors are concerned, the population at large seems to recognise that their own individual, everyday experience does not quite match up to what they read in the papers; where they have to balance these two types of information they tend to favour their own experience. As Onora O'Neill said in her Reith lecture a few years ago: 'The pursuit of ever more perfect accountability provides citizens and consumers, patients and parents with more information, more comparisons, more complaints systems, but also builds a culture of suspicion, low morale and may ultimately lead to professional cynicism and then we would have grounds for public mistrust'.[11]

Of course this is no reason for complacency and I am certainly not trying to suggest that doctors are beyond reproach. We can ill afford to be complacent and have to look hard at whether we deserve the trust placed in us.

At the end of the day we have to ensure that we are worthy of all this trust that patients have in us and show that we are earning it – given the uncomfortable fact that, no matter how many good doctors there are, and no matter how well regulated they are, there will always be the odd renegade who acts immorally, illegally or despicably. After all, the full panoply of human behaviour will always exist among doctors as among any other group. We do seem to survive despite these anxieties and we are fortunate that personal experiences are generally acceptable and usually good. More on this topic later in Chapter 11.

Extending the Lasdun Building

As the RCP extended its activities and increased the number of its staff it was becoming obvious that our buildings, into which the RCP had moved in 1966, were uncomfortably cramped. We desperately needed a new council chamber and a second lecture theatre.

The 1966 building, designed by Denys Lasdun, in Regent's Park had become iconic. A listed building and very modern, in the Lasdun style, it stood out among the Regency terraces. Most of Lasdun's buildings made much use of highly visible concrete, as, for example, at the National Theatre. The only nod he gave to softening the appearance of our particular building had been the small white tiles in which it was clad. There were still many aspects where the characteristic Lasdun concrete crept in, but the harshness was softened by the cladding. The story goes that, when Robert Platt, president in the 1960s, had been seeking an architect for the new College, he took Lasdun to the window of the College, then in Canada House in Trafalgar Square. He pointed to the National Gallery saying, 'Will you build us something like that?' Lasdun answered that there was no way he could build such a 'monstrosity'. Platt then said, 'Good, you're on!'

Lasdun took a very keen interest in our building and was a constant visitor. He was very strict with us if we proposed even a minor change to what he regarded as his building. It was with great trepidation then that I plucked up all my courage and approached him about designing an extension.

I need not have feared. He was delighted and immediately pulled open a wide drawer in which he had a plan for just the extension we wanted. Apparently he had predicted, when he designed the original building, that we would one day need an extension. The design was a pure delight. It included a magnificent round council chamber and a tiered lecture theatre below it. The design was extremely clever because it looked as if it was part of the original building and not an add-on extension.

Furthermore, the council chamber, sited off the central hall, was directly opposite the Censors Room which had been transferred to the new building intact from the 18th century college in Warwick Lane. Lasdun explained, in one of his lectures to the RCP, that as one walked across from one side of the hall to the other you were moving across the centuries.

I was still president when the new extension was opened in 1997 and was able to welcome Princess Anne to perform the opening ceremony.

Spreading the message

One of the challenges facing the RCP when I took up office was the accusation that it was very London-centric, despite the fact that three of the previous four presidents had arrived from the provinces. I was happy to try to correct that perception by spending time on regional visits. I travelled around the UK, meeting fellows and chairing open meetings, but it became increasingly clear that this was going to be insufficient to meet fellows' needs. It was this that prompted us to open the first regional office of the RCP in Newcastle. This turned out to be such a success that, later, several more were opened around the country.

We had a pair of regional advisers in each region of the country and each hospital had a college tutor. I instigated a regular meeting of advisers and tutors, and this also helped cement relations between the RCP and the regions. I am not sure if we made a big difference but it might be relevant that two of the next three presidents were also from the provinces.

Professional divisions

Other divisions were opening up to which I had to turn my attention. Some of the specialist societies, representing a considerable number and variety of specialties in medicine, felt marginalised, even though the RCP fellowship and council were made up of representatives of all these specialties. I tried to bring the specialist societies on board by arranging regular meetings with officers of all of them. This helped but there were always some who agitated for a separate college of their own. We managed to head this off for the geriatricians but were ultimately unsuccessful with the paediatricians.

Losing the 'children': the paediatric college

During much of my presidency the pressure was building for the paediatricians to split off and form a college of their own. I tried very hard to persuade them that it was not in their, or our, best interests to divide the RCP in this way, and made myself somewhat unpopular in so doing. My argument was that they were well cared for in the single large college with its greater clout in dealing with the government and other external bodies. Furthermore the paediatricians were well represented with Dame June Lloyd, Sir David Hull and John Dodge as successive vice-presidents and Robert Boyd as academic registrar. They had a separate paediatric MRCP examination as well as members of council. I could not see the loss of such valued colleagues with much equanimity.

I also believed that we already had too many colleges with no fewer than three colleges of physicians, including two in Scotland, and 12 others. The colleges were often fragmented and found difficulty in speaking with one voice if we needed to present our case to government. The last thing we needed was yet another college.

In the end I could not divert them from their course. It was thought by some that I was disaffected by the paediatricians when in fact it was my strong desire to keep them within the bosom of the physicians, with whom they had so much in common, that determined my position and not any antipathy towards them. However it was with some hesitation that Ken Calman, then chief medical officer, phoned some time later to ask if I would try to block the new college's effort to be given a royal charter. I was able to reassure him that as they now had a college I wanted to form as close a relationship with them as possible. I wished them every success and of course, they would have my full support for a royal charter.

I was surprised, but gratified, later when I was invited to speak after dinner at their inaugural annual meeting in York. As I said then: 'The fact that I am here speaks volumes for the human capacity for forgiveness'.

Foreign affairs

During my five years as president I was fortunate enough to lead the RCP on a number of visits to overseas colleges. South Africa, Australia, Singapore, Pakistan, Malaysia, Hong Kong and the USA were all included in our itinerary and I tried hard to cement relationships in each country. Lavish receptions as well as scientific meetings were usually interesting, and I was embarrassed by being given an honorary fellowship of some sort at each visit. These, together with an increasing number of honorary fellowships from a variety of UK colleges, rapidly became somewhat meaningless. This may sound ungrateful but UK colleges were busily giving fellowships to each other's presidents. Mine were all awarded simply because I was president of our college and not because of anything special that I might have done. It was difficult to know what to do with this largesse of diplomas, some of which were magnificently embossed. Clearly they could not be framed and displayed, and in the end they were all rolled up in tubes gathering dust under a pile of books in a corner of my study. How ungrateful that sounds, but I remain unconvinced that I had earned any of these rewards.

I was knighted in 1994 and of course I was delighted to be honoured in this way. Edna, too, was pleased but could not take it too seriously and went out of her way to avoid being referred to as a 'Lady'. I realised that as a president of the physicians I would have been unique if I had not been knighted. All my predecessors had been so dubbed, apart, that is, from those given a peerage, so I considered that it came with the job and I should not be too impressed with myself.

Mergers and divisions

Conference of Colleges and the birth of the Academy of Medical Royal Colleges

The failure of the colleges to agree joint strategies had long been a problem and had certainly not eased by the time I came into office. My predecessor, Margaret Turner-Warwick, had tried hard to keep the colleges together during her two years as chairman of the Conference of Colleges. This organisation was an informal body made up of all the college presidents. The chairman had to be supported by the secretariat of his or her own college because this loose association of presidents was unable to employ any staff. Each president, not unexpectedly, felt that his or her allegiance should be to his or her own college and was unwilling to agree to anything discussed at meetings of the Conference of Colleges without first going back to their councils. Councils in turn were suspicious of what their presidents were 'deciding' at the Conference of Colleges when in effect they were not deciding anything at all.

Peter Lachmann, a past president of the Royal College of Pathologists, had tried, with Margaret, to formalise the Conference of Colleges, and put it on a stronger basis but to no avail. College presidents were always reluctant to cede any power or responsibility to another body once they had been elected to high office in their own sphere. In this there was an uncanny resemblance to the EU and the agonies of individual member states as they struggle with subsidiarity principles and the like.

In my second year I was elected to chair the Conference of Colleges and did so for the next two years. I realised that, although presidents were the sole representatives of their college's views, there would always be difficulties in getting decisions agreed. I thought that it might be more productive if each president came with either the registrar or college secretary to sit with them. In this way I thought that college council suspicions could be allayed and presidents would be better briefed and able to take decisions. It was all too simplistic and I was saddened that the idea never took off.

I turned my attention to trying to make the Conference of Colleges a formal body with funds, derived from the colleges, to employ staff to produce agendas and minutes, and, most importantly, to make and record decisions. I made an effort to prepare my own college by referring to the need for the colleges to speak with one voice when I spoke in council and at many a dinner. It took virtually all of my two years to reach agreement with the other colleges and it was achieved only because of a new development that threatened to remove much of what little power colleges had.

This took the form of a threat by the EU Commission to take infraction proceedings against the British government unless it changed the way in which postgraduate medical education was overseen. In particular the UK had to set up a 'competent body' that would ensure that medical education here complied with the minimum standards set across all EU member states. I come in a moment to the way in which we were able to deal with this problem, but here I indicate how it impacted on the need for the colleges to form a more cohesive and effective body.

The General Medical Council (GMC) had had oversight of undergraduate medical education since the Act of 1858, but supervision of postgraduate training and education had remained the province of the medical royal colleges. This was now threatened as the government began to seek a competent body to take over postgraduate training and, as the colleges held this responsibility only in a non-statutory way, it was not at all clear that it would be them. It was now obvious that the colleges needed to come together as a single, formal body if they were to be considered as 'competent'. There was no way that the government would consider the possibility of multiple 'competent bodies' each represented by individual colleges. Overcoming some reluctance, and driven by necessity, I managed to convince my co-presidents that we should become an incorporated body and that we should call ourselves the 'Council of Medical Royal Colleges'. Few liked this name and in the end we opted for the 'Academy of Medical Royal Colleges' (AMRC). Of course, we were not an academy in any normal meaning of the word, but it sounded business-like. So, at long last, in 1997, we were pushed into an uneasy but essential legal alliance. We each paid our dues, hired an executive officer and rented accommodation at the Royal Society of Medicine.

Not everyone outside the colleges appreciated the name as much as the colleges did. I was also involved at the time with others, in early discussions about the formation of another academy, the Academy of Medical Sciences, and some felt that we had stolen a march in using the term 'academy' for the colleges. I was able to point out that there really was no conflict and later events proved this to be the case. The aims and responsibilities of the two academies were widely different and there was no possibility of any confusion.

At first the AMRC became a little more focused in its activities but I fear that, over the years since then, it has not always been seen as a major force. Individual presidents tend not to turn to the AMRC for concerted action and rely, as ever, on individual approaches to government and other authorities. It is the case now that when ministers or parliamentarians turn for a view from the colleges they usually look to individual colleges and not to the AMRC. Colleges may be quoted in *Hansard* but rarely, if ever, the AMRC. Clearly my ambitions for it have not been entirely fulfilled. Some recent proposals emerging from the AMRC on 'seven-day' working have been taken up by the government, but even here it has been the chairman who has been quoted in parliament as an individual.

More mergers and the formation of the MERCC

I seemed to have the knack of overseeing the birth of bodies that turn out not to be as effective or long lasting as I had hoped. There were two more such bodies: the Medical Education and Research Co-ordinating Committee (MERCC) and the Specialist Training Authority of the Medical Royal Colleges (STA).

I worked to bring together, in the MERCC, those organisations concerned with the different phases of medical education, in the belief that it should be a continuous process from entry into medical school until retirement. The MERCC was formed as a collaborative body comprising medical school deans (Council of Deans), the Committee of Postgraduate Medical Deans (COPMED) and the AMRC. I chaired it in its first phase and it seemed, super-ficially at least, to fulfil a need. Attendance, however, was always patchy and after a few years its informality led to its abandonment. Unless there is strong leadership and unity of purpose, and each organisation in such a collaborative body feels that there is some value to their attendance, they are likely to be doomed. I have seen this with many organisations which, unless they have a clear agenda for decision and action, tend to fade and die. I have also noticed that government departments sometimes devolve difficult decisions to such committees to avoid any action.

The MERCC did, however, perform one extremely valuable function in setting up the implementation committee that led to the Academy of Medical Sciences; more of that later.

Regulating the profession and formation of the Specialist Training Authority

In contrast to the other bodies I have described, the STA did have a set of formal statutory responsibilities and had both staff and outputs. Its beginnings are fascinating and the fact that the colleges became an integral part of it was due to a number of fortunate coincidences.

The chief medical officer at the Department of Health, Kenneth Calman, had recently introduced new regulations about specialist training and in particular had proposed a marked shortening of the time needed to train a specialist. This had raised all sorts of hackles among the profession although, in truth, the length of training was largely determined by the availability of consultant posts at the end of training, rather than being educationally desirable. However, for all the attention given to the changes outlined in the Calman report, they were prompted by the need not so much to improve training but rather to circumvent the problem faced by the British government when it found itself on the wrong side of European legislation. In the UK, two standards for training specialists had long been in place: those wishing to practise in the UK had to spend longer before being accredited than those who, although training here, wished to enter specialist practice in another European member state. Quite apart from the seemingly arrogant assumption that a lower standard would do for the rest of Europe, this practice had long been in breach of the 1975 European directives concerned with the free flow of the workforce across state boundaries. The introduction of a single standard and length of specialist training, and the harmonisation of minimum criteria for training across Europe, meant that the British government was off the hook of potential infraction proceedings being taken against it.

There remained, however, the need to set up a regulatory body to take responsibility for ensuring that specialist training in the UK met the requirements laid down in European directives and orders. But who should take on the role of this 'competent body'?

Although the royal colleges had had the responsibility for setting the standards for, and supervision of, postgraduate education and training, they had no statutory basis for this responsibility. They had assumed these roles under their charters, but were not backed by any legal authority. Indeed they had lost all such authority for medical education with the 1858 Act that saw the GMC taking over as the licensing body for undergraduate education from the RCP and the Royal College of Surgeons. Although the colleges may have hoped, and even assumed, that they might form the new statutory body for postgraduate training, this was not necessarily the way others saw it.

Proposals by the Department of Health and the NHS Executive were crystallised in a draft document circulated during October 1994 in which it was suggested that the GMC would be designated the competent authority to issue certificates of completion of specialist training. Included in the competent authority's responsibilities were all those currently undertaken by the colleges. It was obvious that this proposal would result in a very unfavourable position for the colleges. It would leave them firmly under the control of the GMC.

Further, it would leave the GMC free to look to other potential providers of postgraduate education including postgraduate deans and universities. I viewed this type of relationship with the GMC as being precarious and one that would make the colleges more vulnerable. As their main raison d'être was setting standards through education and training, the loss of these functions could leave them irretrievably damaged.

Intense discussions took place during the remainder of 1994 and early 1995, and legal advice was sought. I, as chairman of the Conference of Colleges, and Sir Robert Kilpatrick, the president of the GMC, were fortunately in full agreement that the proposals were not workable as they stood and these opinions were endorsed by the chief medical officer (CMO). The way was therefore open for another competent body or bodies to take on responsibility for specialist medical training.

Initially we made two proposals. The first was for every college to form its own competent body and the other was that the Conference of Colleges, or nascent Academy of Royal Colleges itself, might be the competent body. The former was immediately rejected by the Department of Health as being far too bureaucratic. It soon became clear too that, for the Conference of Colleges to be the competent body, it would have to become a statutory body, take on legal responsibilities and limit its roles in other interests of the colleges.

Thus, it emerged that a separate and distinct body made up largely of representatives of the colleges would provide the most acceptable basis for a statutory authority, at least as far as the colleges were concerned.

There were of course a number of potential hazards. Colleges would become legally liable for their actions. They would have to comply with EU and UK law, and the secretary of state would have the power to intervene if the colleges acted in a way that would make the government liable to legal proceedings against it. Despite these potential hazards, it was clear that the colleges could not realistically avoid taking responsibility for the actions that they had been undertaking under their charters, and that any other body taking it on would place them in an impossible position.

The support of Robert Kilpatrick, during his last year as president of the GMC, was critical. Donald Irvine, who followed Robert as president of the GMC a short time later, had quite different ideas and would never have agreed to our taking on this role. This became evident later when the STA had been established and he started snapping at our heels.

After Robert's approval it was then up to us to persuade the CMO, Ken Calman, and the Department of Health. Ken was an ally in our efforts and needed little persuasion. The Department of Health, however, was full of officials who were not overwhelmed by admiration for the colleges. They regarded us more as irritants, if not irrelevant to the running of the health service. I well remember going, with Norman Browse, president of the Royal College of Surgeons, to see the then minister, Gerald Malone, who met us with one of his minions. We made our case and much to our surprise he turned to his discomforted civil servant and said: 'Well, that sounds OK doesn't it?' And that was it.

Here, for the first time in the history of the colleges, they were being given legal responsibility for postgraduate specialist education and training, responsibilities that they had simply assumed in practice until then. It had been a precarious position for the colleges that could have had their roles taken from them and given to the GMC at any time. Until then, that is, when we suddenly had it for ourselves.

The momentous nature of this achievement seemed to pass some of the colleges by. They regarded this new body with suspicion. Some were more concerned with the realisation that the new body would take over some of their individual responsibilities than with the notion of what had been won. I insisted that, although we were known as the STA, our full title was Specialist Training Authority of the Medical Royal Colleges in order to indicate where we were coming from.

We were fortunate in that the Department of Health seconded Lesley Hawksworth to us as our first chief executive. She was the civil servant in the department who had been deeply immersed in the nuances of the directive under which the new competent body was set up and she kept us all on a straight path as we moved into action.

I had relinquished my chairmanship of the Academy of Royal Colleges a year before the STA came into being, and indicated that I would prefer to concentrate my efforts on the formation of the STA. There was a little political intrigue in which Fiona Caldicott, president of the Royal College of Psychiatrists and then chairman of the Academy, tried to take on the role of chairman of the STA, something that I had spent considerable effort in setting up. I was, however, elected by a considerable majority.

I continued in the role of chairman of the STA for about two years and was succeeded by Naren Patel, past president of the Royal College of Obstetricians, and later Lord Patel.

Problems for the STA

From its beginnings the STA was in variable degrees of conflict with the colleges despite it being their offspring and having their full involvement. The reasons were clear. The role of the STA was a legal one and it was required to ensure that the curricula for each specialty matched at least the minimum standards, specifically in terms of the duration of the course, set by the EU. This required each of the colleges to submit their curricula to the STA for inspection, a somewhat demeaning exercise as far as they were concerned. The colleges always presumed that the standards of training that they oversaw were second to none. It came as a shock that, from time to time, submitted documents were sent back to them for further work. They were just not used to being told what to do.

I was fairly laid back about the documentation but neither I nor the colleges were allowed to take even a small step outside the boundaries set by Lesley H, who was a veritable tiger for detail. Her civil service training lent a certain rigidity to her approach and that was only appropriate as we moved into the new arrangements.

In due course the system began to work reasonably well but there were always 'issues'. Of these the most problematic was how to deal with trainees in academic posts when they were not in full-time training as they pursued their research at the same time. As the main criterion that the EU directive required us to fulfil was time spent in training, we were hidebound by this requirement. This criterion created major problems and how we counted time in non-clinical activities taxed our flexibility.

The second difficulty arose when non-EU, overseas academics wanted to work in the UK. Trying to get a measure of their training was often difficult. Taking account of experience against formal training was problematic, and our ability to make compromises under the rigid bureaucracy that we were obliged to operate was sorely tested. These caused rather more antipathy than I was happy with but as time passed we managed to adjust even to this situation.

We did not incorporate the general practitioners (GPs) who had their own competent body, the JCPTGP (Joint Committee on Postgraduate Training for General Practice). I always thought that it was anomalous that we had separate bodies but I felt that I had enough to do without tackling the GPs.

It was then that Donald Irving began to stretch his muscles at the GMC and tried to nibble away at our responsibilities. Should we be the body giving out certificates of competence to trainees? What about the GMC's statutory responsibility to 'coordinate all phases of medical education and training'? Doesn't that mean that we, the STA, should seek their approval before agreeing to certify that we are satisfied with a doctor's training? I had to point out that the STA was itself a statutory body with its own competence to award such certificates. A letter I wrote to him at the time set out our position vis-à-vis the GMC's position. I wrote:

Clearly we should try to work closely together while recognising that each has our own individual areas of competence. It will be important in so doing to have an understanding between us about our relative roles and responsibilities. The competence of the STA is to ensure that specialist training complies with the specialist order and that training meets the requirements set out in colleges' curricula and standards. The GMC on the other hand, with its responsibilities for standards and for maintaining the register of specialists, will, no doubt, wish to draw the attention of the STA to problems that it perceives in the effectiveness, or lack of it, in specialist practice as a result of this training. The STA and the colleges will, of course, always be open to such advice. However, the relationship between the GMC and the STA will not be quite like that between the GMC and the medical schools in that neither body will expect the GMC to be in the position of approving or not the content or methods of training or of curricular changes. Nor do I imagine will the GMC be in the position of inspecting or approving postgraduate examinations and assessments run by the colleges. These lie within the competence and responsibilities of the STA colleges. I imagine that all this is straightforward but I do believe that it is important to set down what we understand as our respective areas of responsibility so that we can work together. I hope you agree.

He was never very happy about the situation but we remained on reasonably friendly terms.

The end of the STA

In a short history of the origins of the STA written in 1999, I said:

The occasional irritation (with the way the STA operated) is mitigated by the realization that the alternatives to the STA, that might so easily have been imposed, could have been more difficult to endure. However, the Specialist Medical Order can be amended by the secretary of state without recourse to parliament and can be amended at will.

Sadly, that is what was to happen.

In 2005 the STA was merged with the JCPTGP to form the Postgraduate Medical Education and Training Board (PMETB), bringing the specialists and GPs under one body. Although this was an entirely rational merger, the PMETB never fully gained the confidence of the colleges or profession.

More unfortunately, the PMETB was swept up in later onslaughts on the GMC by the Labour government. It was dragged along in the veritable tsunami of change that followed several years after I had left the RCP and was already in the Lords.

The GMC had come under some criticism (not entirely deserved I felt) in the wake of the Shipman affair. A GP, Dr Shipman, in Hyde, near Manchester, had killed a number of elderly patients and it was believed that somehow the GMC should have had systems in place that would prevent murder by doctors. It is difficult to know how the GMC could have added any greater criminality to acts of murder or how it could ever stop a determined murderer from killing people. Nor do I imagine that a doctor keen on murder could be detected if he or she is clever enough. Nevertheless some blame was attached to the GMC and the government felt that public pressure should be heeded somehow. The GMC was already the subject of criticism by a public that thought that it was too lenient on misbehaving doctors and by the medical profession that felt that it was too severe. Reform of the GMC was inevitable and at the same time, as its numbers were being reduced and lay representation increased, it was felt, for not very obvious reasons, that its roles in medical education should also be changed.

Until then the education committee of the GMC was governed under a separate statute. It was responsible directly to the Privy Council and only indirectly to the GMC. Although it was not the subject of any criticism and had been performing its task of overseeing undergraduate education entirely to everyone's satisfaction, it too was swept up in the reforms. Its separation from the GMC was removed, it became a subcommittee of the GMC itself, and its membership and agenda became determined by the GMC.

Here we had a situation in which a perfectly satisfactory organisation was to be transferred into another that was widely regarded as unsatisfactory. Not a recipe for success and not one that any other business, apart from government that is, would adopt.

It might be asked what this had to do with the PMETB? All became clear when, in this overarching tidying up exercise, the government proposed that the PMETB should also be taken over by the GMC and placed within its education committee. The rationale for this move was that all phases of medical education should be treated as one, even though existing systems were working reasonably satisfactorily. It should have been obvious to the colleges that they were about to lose their hard-won legal responsibility for postgraduate education. Furthermore, that responsibility was to be handed over to a GMC that was about to be dominated, not by doctors, but by a lay membership selected by the secretary of state for health and without educational expertise in its membership. This was to be a body that had direct responsibility to the secretary of state and I could see that, if he or she felt that doctors should be trained differently somehow, here was the instrument with which he or she could make it happen. I imagined a scenario in which there was a failure by a doctor to care properly for a child somewhere in England and there was a public outcry. The secretary of state would be under some pressure to do something about it and he or she immediately turns to the GMC and tells them to change the curriculum and make sure that all paediatricians have a course of remedial training. Thus political expediency could determine curricular change without regard to its validity.

I tried to persuade the college presidents of these dangers but I fear that their minds must have been elsewhere. Perhaps they thought I exaggerated the dangers when I spoke to them at the AMRC, and it is possible that they are correct.

Indeed, so far, my worst fears have not been realised but I cannot avoid thinking that the colleges were somewhat inert in their response to this major shift in their fortunes. They were about to lose a statutory responsibility that gave them security, but their minds were elsewhere. There is now no legal basis for their existence and their roles can be taken over at any time by the universities, GMC or postgraduate deans in any combination. Indeed the recent development of local education and training boards, made up of hospital trusts and universities, that will oversee medical education and training, might well see the colleges increasingly marginalised. Unfortunately, in the absence of any college interest or support, it became impossible for me to argue their case in the Lords. To my mind this was a very sad development and another of the battles that I felt I had lost. I fear for the future of the colleges and their roles under the new regime.

EU directives and the tragic case of a missed opportunity

One of the more convoluted affairs with which I had to deal as chairman of the STA concerned the need to allow the free flow of workers, including medical specialists, across the borders of EU member states. The government was anxious to do as much as possible to demonstrate good neighbourliness within the EU in as many 'non-essential' areas as possible. Freedom for doctors from other EU countries to come to practise in the UK was regarded as one of those easy wins, even though we knew next to nothing of the training that those doctors had received.

It was said that, as we now had a system in which there was some uniformity of training requirements across the EU, problems should not arise if, for example, a Greek, French or Italian cardiac surgeon or paediatrician came to work in the UK. As we knew about the minimum length of training, in years, that EU doctors had received, this was deemed sufficient by the Department of Health, even though we knew nothing of the content of those training programmes. Specialist medical curricula that we had evolved and used to ensure high standards in our own trainees were disregarded in the rush to comply with EU directives.

We were not to be allowed to assess any individual doctor's skills, knowledge or aptitudes once they had a certificate of competence from their own country.

We were then in the ridiculous, and to my mind potentially dangerous, situation in which we were obliged to thoroughly vet the training that Australian and American specialists had received, about which we were pretty well aware, but not the training of doctors from other European countries, about which we were in total ignorance.

I well remember a meeting at the Home Office, chaired by Jeremy Metters, deputy chief medical officer, and including officials from the Home Office and other state departments. I spoke about the problems for the safety of patient care if we had no way of ensuring the competence of the EU doctors looking after them. It was clear that the civil servants had little idea about the problems I outlined when one of them asked why this was any different from the case of doctors coming to the UK from other countries, for example Brazil. I had to patiently explain that before a Brazilian doctor could go anywhere near a patient in the UK, his previous training would have to be carefully examined and he may well need a period of further training that we could, if necessary, insist upon. I pointed out that it was only member-state doctors who were exempt from this quality-control exercise.

The drive to keep the UK on the right side of the EU overcame any arguments that I made about the small matter of patient safety and I left that meeting feeling very frustrated. I thought that Jeremy Metters had let our patients down.

I struggled hard to tackle these difficulties although I felt very much alone in arguing the case for greater safeguards. When I requested sight of training curricula from training bodies, where they existed, in other states, I received no responses. I presumed that they just could not be bothered or, worse, they did not have any formal written programmes. We were back to a situation where we would have to accept any specialist to practise in the UK without knowledge of what their training comprised. Any attempt to assess their competencies would be regarded as contrary to EU directives.

The only stage at which an applicant for a UK consultant post could be questioned was at interview for that post. If they happened to be the only applicant and they had completed their legally defined length of training elsewhere in Europe, then there would be little a potential employer could do but accept them. This has led to a number of difficulties, particularly in the privately run day-case surgery centres that sprang up to help reduce 'waiting list' problems a few years ago. Some thought that the doctors brought in for this purpose were not always of the highest standard.

There was one further potential safeguard of standards that we could have introduced and that is what I strived to achieve next. Here opposition was fierce.

There were two systems in operation by which it would be possible to fulfil the directive on movement of professionals across the EU. The first, the sectoral systems directive, was the one that the Department of Health and the British Medical Association (BMA) favoured and involved simply accepting the qualifications of EU specialists, about whose training we knew little apart from the fact that they had completed the minimum number of years. The other, the general systems directive, allowed member states to make some assessment of professionals' training and to request a period of further experience before they could take up a post if their training differed substantially from that required of UK trainees. The latter seemed to me to be a valuable way round our difficulties. That view, however, was not shared by the BMA or the Royal College of General Practitioners, although most of the other colleges seemed unclear about the significance of these admittedly complex matters.

At a meeting I chaired in November 1997, I set out the advantages and disadvantages of the two systems as fairly as I could to an audience of the BMA, the Department of Health and the colleges: the sectoral system was simple to administer because mutual recognition was virtually automatic; it was cheaper; it had been accepted by a number of member states; and it had been accepted by several other UK professions including dentists and GPs. Its disadvantages were: the criteria focus on time spent in training and not on content of training programmes; amending the directive to take account of changes in training was lengthy and unwieldy; and increased membership of the EU would leave the UK and other member states in the dark about the nature of training in any new member states.

The advantages of the general systems approach that I favoured included: doctors could be asked to undertake a period of 'adaptation' and tests if their training differed substantially from that of the host state; flexibility in the assessment of training; more rapid movement towards competency-based training; ability to take on new member states; and applicants would be dealt with fairly and without prejudice at appointments committees. Disadvantages included: extra costs; and an additional bureaucratic load on competent bodies.

I described the problems and potential solution but was opposed by the BMA in particular. Their arguments were, first, that the GPs were happy with the simpler process of recognition because they were fully informed of the training of their equivalents in the rest of Europe. They may have been influenced by the fact that there are few equivalents to primary care in other EU countries and few, if any, would come to practise in the UK. One of them did so a year or so ago and was shown to be clearly inadequately trained for general practice after a tragic mishap. Second, the dentists were also happy with what they knew of dental training across Europe but in this case they were interested primarily in undergraduate qualifications and not postgraduate specialists. Finally it was said that it would be impossible for one group of doctors, the specialists, to have a different system of recognition from the others. And, of course, it would mean more work.

I, on the other hand, had had discussions in Brussels with the relevant officials responsible for this directive and had learnt that there was no reason at all why different branches of the profession could not use different systems of recognition. Furthermore, I knew that the opticians and other professions allied to medicine had chosen to take on the more 'invasive' system that I favoured for specialists. Indeed the Commission's official, Jaqueline Minors, strongly agreed with my arguments and advised me to pursue the issue at home.

Despite presenting my case as best I could, and despite what I took to be its logic, I had to admit defeat. I was accused of scaremongering and that I would be the first to blow a whistle when an EU-trained specialist prescribed the wrong drug or performed a wrong operation.

The BMA and John Cash, who was also president of the Royal College of Physicians of Edinburgh, remained antipathetic to my proposals. The hostilities slowly subsided but, by then, in 1997, we had been forced to accept the simple but, to my mind, deeply flawed system of mutual recognition.

Very belatedly there has been a recent resurgence of interest in the standards of training of EU doctors and concerns have been expressed focusing not just on knowledge of the English language.

In 2011 the EU Commission itself issued a Green Paper on revising the professional qualifications register and the House of Lords Select Committee on the EU produced a report on *Safety first: mobility of healthcare professionals in the EU.* Baroness Young, chairman of that committee, said in the debate in the Lords on 22 March 2012:

> *We also recognised that the current directive failed to command the confidence of patients and professionals. Major UK regulators, including the General Medical Council and the Nursing and Midwifery Council expressed strong concerns in their evidence to us that discrepancies in the current system forced them to admit individuals who did not meet the standards otherwise required of U.K. or non-EEA professionals, thereby putting patients at potentially serious risk. Incidents related to failures of the directive have been statistically low. However, high profile examples have had fatal results. This has undermined confidence in the directive and led to fears in some quarters that mobility has been prioritised over patient safety.*[12]

Pressure by the GMC has resulted in two helpful changes to the directives that are being debated. Doctors arriving fresh from the EU will now have to pass an English language test – a useful advance – but they will have to take such a test only after they have been registered as fit to practise.

The Commission has also been persuaded to institute an early warning system so that notification of a doctor misbehaving in one country can be passed to all other member states' authorities.

Unfortunately, however, it has not proved possible to fill the gap in information about training. It is extremely unlikely that the British government, even if it were willing, would be able to convince all the other EU countries to change to the general systems directive which would provide access to information about the content of training. We will have to continue to rely on vetting EU doctors when they apply for consultant posts. The new system of 'responsible officers', introduced in 2011, for the assessment of all doctors' practice and their capacity to take responsibility for their clinical roles, may offer an approach for assessing EU entrants. Time will tell if this is a practicable solution, although I am doubtful if it will be easy to cope with the workload.

The alternative may be the French approach, which is to ignore the directives and make all non-French EU doctors serve an apprenticeship for a year! Rather late, in any case, to be taking corrective action, 15 years after we started out on this wrong, and now recognised to be dangerous, track. I fully acknowledge my failure to persuade my colleagues at the time of the damaging course we were taking. It was not, however, for want of trying.

End of the presidency

I decided to stand down at the end of my fifth year in office. The presidents of all the other colleges were appointed for a maximum of three years whereas in my college the president faced re-election each year for as long as he or she desired to stay in office.

Those in the role before the 1950s often stayed for very many years. Lord Moran remained in post for 11 years, although his election was contested by a disillusioned Lord Horder in 1947, when support of the RCP for the proposed new National Health Service was being questioned. Moran won by six votes.

In recent times a five-year term was about average and no sitting president had been challenged. This meant that either the president was behaving reasonably well or the inertia among the fellows was too great. It would be embarrassing to have to ask a sitting president to stand down and embarrassment should be avoided at all costs at the RCP. We were fortunate in having a succession of men and a woman who led the RCP with great distinction, so embarrassment was never an issue.

Five-year terms had advantages and disadvantages. It was valuable to have more than three years because the first year is spent getting over the shock of being elected and learning where the traps lie, the second year doing the job and the third as something of a lame duck as a successor is sought. It was helpful too to be longer in office than presidents of other colleges in that you are more experienced than most for at least half your time. The disadvantage to the RCP was that they were stuck with someone who may or may not be the leader whom they had hoped for. For the individual, at least for me, the fifth year becomes an increasing burden as the duties become more and more repetitive. Five years of membership and fellowship admission ceremonies at four each per year, with innumerable handshakes and an increasingly fixed smile, each followed by dinner and yet more speeches, can weary the most enthusiastic of individuals. And I was becoming tired. I had been giving speeches at dinner at a rate of two or three per week and finding something new to say on each occasion had become a near impossibility. Rotating my speeches and trying to keep tabs on what I had said to what audiences was a burden and, although my listeners kept up the impression of being attentive, I found that it was me who was losing attention. I can only guess at how my fellow officers must have felt at having to sit through yet another of my speeches to new members or fellows. Their laughter at the umpteenth repetition of my attempts at a joke must have been a strain. At times like these I realised how valuable the enormous support was that I had had during my whole time as president from David London as registrar and Norman Jones and then John Bennett, as treasurers of the RCP.

After I had left the RCP the rules were changed so that presidents were to be allowed to sit only for a maximum of four years although they still had to submit to an election each year. I do not think this rule change had anything to do with my having seemed to overstay my welcome but one never knows.

I was conscious that the fifth year was to be my last and I began to heave little sighs of relief that I had come through it without any major disasters. I could not have known that something awful was about to blow up during the election of my successor.

One of the RCP rules was that no candidate should canvas for votes. The idea was that they should be sufficiently well known among the fellows and they should not need to dirty their hands with the shady business of touting for votes. Friends may put in a good word but that should be without the knowledge or cognisance of candidates themselves. This seems to have been a reasonable and acceptable system when there were 100 or so fellows but by the time my successor was due to be elected we had more than 8,000 fellows and many lived abroad. There was no way candidates could be known by the whole electorate and it was clear that a different approach was required. Most candidates simply relied on friends and colleagues to spread the message. Some, however, over-stepped the mark in my successor's election and self-publicity became irres-istible to them. I will not mention names but a senior fellow, together with one candidate, accused another candidate of blatant personal canvassing. I then found myself having to seek assurances from all six candidates that they had not been canvassing. My fear was that we would find the RCP at the centre of a scan-dal with one or more candidates having to be banned from the election. My heart sank when we discovered that one had indeed seemed to have canvassed for himself and another had promoted others to canvas for him.

There is a procedure for dealing with such an eventuality, of which I was completely unaware but that the college secretary, Bernard Lloyd, was able to dig out from the archives. This involved setting up a committee of enquiry made up of three fellows and myself as chairman. Both candidates were then interviewed at length, an embarrassing business in the extreme because both were colleagues. In the end, after a deal of agonising there seemed to the committee to be some extenuating circumstances for each of them. Their case was helped by the lack of clarity in our bye-laws about what exactly canvassing meant for the RCP.

There were three options open to us. We could banish the miscreants from the election, we could admonish them in writing or we could simply clear them of any misdeed. We chose the middle route of admonishment and the election proceeded as normal.

My final fear was whether any of the fellows who had complained would get up and object on election day. I took the direct route by announcing, immediately before we proceeded to the election, that an enquiry had been held into certain aspects of the election and nothing had been discovered that would prevent the election taking place. I heaved a sigh of relief as no one objected and on we went.

It may sound now, long after the event, like a storm in a teacup but at the time I felt this episode could have sullied my presidency. It so happens that neither of the accused was elected and George Alberti, who succeeded me, had behaved impeccably so far as canvassing was concerned.

We had introduced another change in this election. Only a small proportion of the fellowship can manage to attend the College on election day and the problem with which we struggled was how to maintain the enjoyable atmos-phere in the College on the day while at the same time opening up the election to those who could not attend.

In a typical compromise we engineered a solution that involved regional election centres around the country for all fellows except those who wished to vote at the College on the day. Election day was more complicated and prolonged because it involved not only the traditional way of counting the votes of those attending but amalgamating these with the votes from all the other centres. With two rounds of voting to be held, the second choice votes from the country had to be added to the new votes of those present. If it sounds complicated, it was. But if we thought that it would result in a great increase in the number of fellows voting we were mistaken. The number voting did increase, but only from about 750 in my election to 832 in George Alberti's election. Nevertheless it worked and we were delighted and relieved that it did so.

Birth of the Academy of Medical Sciences

During my time at the RCP other far-reaching developments were afoot and I was heavily involved there too. The Academy of Medical Sciences, long in gestation, was beginning to take clearer shape. Peter Lachmann, whose energy and enthusiasm for the project drove it forward, has written with his typical passion about the birth pangs of the Academy in his book on the topic.[13] Although he was the prime mover, I played some role and he was kind enough to acknowledge that in the book. Here I spend a moment describing my own contribution.

The idea had been around for some time that we, in the UK, should try to set up an organisation akin to the American Institute of Medicine, a prestigious academic body with a distinguished faculty to which the US administration turned for advice.

Peter enlisted my support in view of my positions at the RCP and the Academy of Medical Royal Colleges, bodies that would give vital support. We were of one mind in most things and the proposal for a new scientific body for medicine struck me as being an important gap that should be filled.

There was much suspicion that a new body would take over the roles of others. Yet others dreamt of an overarching organisation that would subsume the whole of medicine, although it rapidly became obvious that that was not only undesirable but also hardly feasible.

The colleges had some interests in academic medicine and research. In my college, at least, all presidents in recent years had been academics and many of our fellows were academics. However, the college had particular responsibility for standards of care rather than purely academic matters.

The BMA had an academic subcommittee and a scientific committee, but its prime responsibility was as a trade union and its main concern was for the terms and conditions of service of its members. The anxiety among those bodies arose because of a fear that the proposed new organisation would stray into their spheres of influence.

A new figure appeared on the scene in the shape of John Brown, chief executive of the Royal Society of Medicine (RSM). He had been asked to act as secretary to the informal group that Peter had set up to pursue the feasibility of a new academy. Unfortunately for us, John had his own agenda and was very keen to find a place for the RSM, preferably at its centre. His idea of an academy was much broader in its roles and responsibilities, and this did nothing to assuage the worries of the BMA or the colleges. Nor did his views coincide with those of the rest of the group and, after a clear difference of opinion opened up, he stood down. The fact that he had personally written to the colleges threatening legal action about their use of the term 'academy' in the recently formed AMRC did not endear him to us at a time when we were anxious to secure the support of the medical profession at large. He also resigned from his position at the RSM at the same time and the whole unhappy episode is described in detail in Peter's book.[13]

It became clear that we needed to come up with a more formal committee of protagonists for the scheme, but who should chair it? Each of us could be seen as biased with our own axes to grind. In a brilliant stroke, Peter suggested that Michael Atya, recently retired president of the Royal Society and a mathematician, was sufficiently independent and, furthermore, interested in helping us, and would be an impeccable person to chair our committee. And so he was.

By that time we had clarified our thinking about what our Academy should focus on. The gap that we all felt was in academic medicine and research. With the degree of certainty that we would not be stepping on the toes of either the BMA or the colleges, we were much more confident that we could get their support. That, however, was not necessarily how they saw it. I had to spend much effort in convincing my own college council that we would not be disadvantaged and that there really was a need for yet another medical organisation in what appeared to be a crowded field. I had somewhat more difficulty convincing the AMRC. In the end, however, they accepted our proposal, provided of course that they would not have to offer any financial support.

Surprisingly, the BMA hierarchy were a little easier to convince. We were fortunate that Sandy Macara was chairman of the BMA council at that time and, once he accepted our case, he became a staunch supporter. Later he became a foundation fellow and editor of the Academy's initial newsletters and publicity material. We then had to set about all the detailed work needed to develop the nascent Academy. We had the support, finally, of the MERCC and its constituent bodies and it was the MERCC that set up an implementation committee with me as its chairman. Its membership included Chris Edwards (then vice provost, Imperial College; later vice chancellor, Newcastle University), Bob Kendell (president, Royal College of Psychiatrists), Naren Patel (then president, Royal College of Obstetricians), John Temple (chairman, Postgraduate Deans) and Peter Lachmann as secretary.

There were legal documents to be drawn up, a method by which the foundation fellowship could be selected and the need to find premises. We decided on an initial fellowship of about 300 and sought nominations from the colleges, the Council of Deans of Medical Schools, COPMED (Postgraduate Deans) and the BMA. Each body selected their share of the 300 with a small number chosen by our committee where there were obvious omissions.

We were favoured by the fortunate coincidence of two valuable opportunities. The first was the support provided by the Wellcome Trust, the chief executive for which, Bridget Ogilvie, was strongly convinced of the case for the academy. It no doubt helped that the board of the Wellcome Trust included a number of founder fellows. The other favourable coincidence came when the British Academy moved to new premises in Carlton House Terrace, a few doors away from the Royal Society. They needed funds to refurbish these premises and had applied for support from the Wellcome Trust. The Trust agreed to their bid, with the proviso that they offered rent-free accommodation for three years for the newly formed Academy of Medical Sciences. So we had premises, an initial fellowship, and a set of legal papers defining our purpose and charitable status.

There remained the issue of defining a system for selection of the first president and officers. Peter was the obvious candidate for the presidency. He, however, was concerned that I might compete for the post. I was chairing the implementation committee and he thought that it would not be unreasonable for me to consider it. I, however, had only recently stood down as president of the RCP and had had enough of presidencies. More importantly, I had no desire to compete with him after all the effort that he had put in to get us to this point, and immediately reassured him that I would not stand. In any event he need not have been concerned because when the votes of the fellowship came in he had a clear majority. I was relieved and he was pleased.

I, however, was elected vice-president, Mark Walport as registrar and Graham Catto as treasurer. Jolyon Oxley became our first executive officer and we were ready for action. Those early years were devoted to establishing ourselves and trying to ensure that we remained solvent. My responsibilities as vice-president were not onerous: supporting the president as necessary and, at the new fellows admission ceremonies, ensuring that they signed the book and then directing them towards the president to receive their diploma.

During the four years that I was vice-president the Academy developed rapidly and it soon became clear that attaching FMedSci after your name was something to be prized.

Election to the fellowship followed the system established by the Royal Society, of which Peter had been a vice-president. After the foundation fellowship had been chosen it became increasingly difficult to be elected. Our reputation grew and we were able to attract applications from the cream of academic medicine and allied sciences.

The Academy's opinion was being sought by government and a number of valuable reports were beginning to be published. As vice-president I was able to contribute to the Academy's activities and felt, after all the prolonged hard work in setting it up, some pride in what had been achieved. Since then it has become an obviously prestigious organisation with a succession of high-profile and able presidents following Peter (Keith Peters, John Bell and John Tooke), who have driven it forward.

It seems that not all the organisations that I helped to set up have disappeared beyond memory.

My grandparents with my father Hyman (*right*), and his siblings Sarah and Mendel (*c.* 1919).

Top: My parents Dolly and Hymie, in Salford (*c.* 1945).

Above: In 1953, while I was at medical school.

Top: In 1973, as a new professor at Hope Hospital (*seen in background*).

Above: My father and I at a farm in Anglesey, Wales (1979).

Top: Visiting the Lake District with Edna (*c.* 1990).
Above: Edna in Florence, Italy (1991).

Receiving knighthood: (*top*) with Daniel, Edna and my mother at Buckingham Palace (1994).

Five presidents of the Royal College of Physicians: (*above, from left*) Sir Raymond (Bill) Hoffenberg, Sir Douglas Black, Sir Cyril Clarke, Dame Margaret Turner-Warwick and me (1995).

Top: Saying something amusing to Norman Jones, former treasurer of the RCP, at a dinner party (1995).

Above: Representing the RCP at the North-West Frontier Province (now known as Khyber Pakhtunkhwa) in Pakistan (1995).

Extending the RCP building in 1995: (*top*) the iconic Council Chamber, under construction; (*above left*) the Seligman Theatre; (*above right*) Sir Denys Lasdun, at the construction site.

Top: Members of the Specialist Training Authority, 1996. (*Top row, from left*) Dr M J Brindle, Professor Charles George, Sir John Temple, Professor Norman MacKay, Dr E B MacDonald, Professor Sandy Muir, Professor Andrew Elkington, Sir Rodney Sweetnam, Dr John Cash, Mr M Winstanley and Professor C Prys-Roberts; (*bottom row, from right*) Professor Barry Jay, Dr June Crown, Dame Fiona Caldicott, Sir Leslie Turnberg, Dr Lotte Newman, Professor Alistair Bellingham, Lesley Hawksworth and Sir Robert Shields.

Above: Receiving Tessa Jowell MP, then minister for public health, on her visit to the Public Health Laboratories in Colindale (1997).

Top: With my mother, on her 90th birthday (2000).

Above: Dolly in 2002.

Top: With our kids Helen and Daniel, in 2003.

Above: Daniel in 2005.

Top: Relaxing at home with Daniel (2005).

Above: Daniel and Edna in Tel Aviv, Israel (2006).

My introduction to the House of Lords in 2000: with Lord John Walton (*left*) and Lord Robert Winston.

Chapter 4 **House of Lords**

The prime minister wonders if you would like to take the Labour whip in the House of Lords?

The phone call from Jonathan Powell came through one evening around 9.30pm late in 1999 as I was watching television. I was confused. What on earth did that mean? I could sympathise with my cousin when, much later, she asked whether I was being whipped or whether I was a cross-dresser.

My knowledge of the Lords was vestigial and Powell suggested that I speak to the chief whip, Lord Carter, to find out more. The House was closed for Christmas and I had to wait until it sat again in mid-January but I was able to sound out one or two friends on what it might mean. When I eventually saw Dennis Carter I was interested in discovering how much time I would be expected to spend in the Lords and what roles I was to play. He was more concerned about whether I was a member of the Labour party and when I admitted that I was not he did not hesitate to say that I had better join. I was not made any the wiser about why I had been elevated in this way. I can only presume that my efforts in the London review of the NHS for Frank Dobson must have had something to do with it (more of that later).

Dennis Carter was able to allay my anxieties about my responsibilities by saying that I would not necessarily have to be in the House all the time. Members are appointed, he said, because of the expertise they bring in from their outside occupations and it was only to be expected that they would continue with those jobs. However, I should try to vote with the government whenever there was a division and if, for some inexplicable reason, I might disagree with a Labour policy I should abstain rather than vote against it.

I knew that the prime minister must have been sitting on the edge of his chair over Christmas waiting for my response, so, with the conditions spelt out, I was able to let Number 10 know that I would be pleased to allay his anxieties and accept the honour.

The world I entered was unlike any in which I had been before and I, like many I suspect, had given it little thought. If I had thought of it at all, it was as a sleepy inert club for elderly distinguished figures. I soon realised that it does a remarkably good job and the country is immeasurably better off for what it achieves.

As a complete outsider it is certainly a confusing place to join and only now, after some 14 years, have I begun to understand a little of its procedures, how it works and, equally important, how to get around the complex warren of corridors, lifts and staircases that lead to hidden dead ends in an archaic but magnificent building.

I quickly learnt how often topics relevant to medicine, health and medical education and research come up in the work of the House. Scarcely a week goes by when there is not a bill, a debate or an oral question that has relevance to medicine. Important examples in the last few years have been the assisted dying bills, the human embryology bill and the human tissue bill, to say nothing of the innumerable health and social care bills.

Within two weeks of entering I found myself giving my maiden speech, on infectious disease, and I have been on my feet every couple of weeks since then. But I never speak without some trepidation. Although there are relatively few doctors, there are experts on every conceivable matter within the House and there are many who have wide experience of the health service or of science, quite apart from the lawyers and ex-ministers who are ever-ready to pick you up if you have your facts wrong. The knowledge base is awesome at times but never less than stimulating. So carefully informed preparation is vital before one speaks.

Although the number of doctors is small, we more than make up for this in our collective contributions to debates. We all speak, some only occasionally whereas others never seem to stop.

It might be asked whether we are effective and do we influence the government at all? I believe that we do have some effect at times. It is particularly the case in medical matters where the government seems to value professional advice – when it suits them.

The primary role of the Lords is as a revising and amending chamber, the purpose of which is to ensure that new legislation coming to it from the Commons is fit for purpose. About 60 per cent of the work of the Lords is concerned with discussion of new legislation in the form of bills and statutory instruments, whereas the remainder is spent on debates and questions. About 10,000 amendments to bills are raised each year, of which about a third are accepted and taken up as bills become acts of parliament.

The Lords spend weeks and sometimes months in debates on the various stages that a bill has to pass through and it is very rare indeed for the act that finally emerges not to have been amended, sometimes quite markedly, as a result. It is here that intervention by the doctors is important and we have been able to introduce a number of changes that I believe have improved bills.

My own interjections have focused largely on health and related matters and on Middle East affairs, particularly where they impinge on Israel. In particular I always seem to be involved in yet another health bill.

I will spend some time shortly expanding on my views of these two themes that have so dominated my life in recent years in the Lords. First, however, I should write something about the possible future of the Lords.

Lords reform

Would the UK population be better served if its parliamentary second chamber were elected rather than selected non-democratically as at present? The population itself has hardly been touched by any interest whatsoever in this far from burning question for them, but that has not stopped it being debated with varying degrees of enthusiasm within parliament for over a century.

During the year before I entered the House, in 1999, what was termed the 'first phase' of Lords reform was accepted. This entailed the removal of a high proportion of hereditary peers from the Lords, leaving just 90 to be elected from among their number. The reasons for leaving this rump of 90 are obscure but entailed a deal between the government and the then leader of the Lords, the Marquess of Salisbury. In any case, it was widely regarded as simply a stage in the process of reform that was due to continue. As might be expected, however, nothing further has happened to the Lords despite much debate. Fourteen years since that first phase is, of course, a very short time when one looks at the long history of efforts to reform. The early years of the 20th century saw much muttering about the powers of the Lords followed by the eponymous Salisbury conventions being enshrined in statute. These curtailed the Lords' powers so that they were deprived of the opportunity to debate treasury bills and they could no longer prevent the democratically elected House of Commons from having its way on bills that were part of the government's manifesto. Then, in 2012, a Lords reform bill reared its head again in the Commons. The Salisbury Conventions would have been sorely tested if the bill had reached the Lords but, as I describe, it was aborted in the Commons.

A major event in Lords reform was the introduction of 'life peerages', that is peers who are selected for the duration of their lives but their peerages are not to be handed on to their children. This decision, in 1958, dramatically changed the ways in which the Upper House went about its activities. It became more business-like and allowed the possibility of bringing in expertise from a wide variety of backgrounds. Nowadays, visitors I take round the Lords marvel at the range of distinguished figures from every walk of life capable of bringing their expertise to bear on our debates.

The last 100 years has, therefore, seen some important, if tortoise-like, movement in Lords' evolution. But the big question of whether the Lords should be elected or remain selected has never gone away. It had never reached the stage of a bill being presented to parliament, until now that is. The argument for election usually focuses on the need to ensure the 'democratic legitimacy' of the second chamber. How can we possibly continue with a system in which a non-democratic chamber of parliament is allowed to decide on the nation's laws?

The argument against that idea that is sometimes used, that it works pretty well as it is so why change it, does not bear close examination because it clearly works well only some of the time and could indeed work much better if it was reformed. But does it need to be elected to achieve this?

A 100 per cent elected chamber is enshrined in the Labour party's policy and manifesto commitment and it is part of the Conservative and Liberal Democrat parties' manifesto too. Except for the Liberal Democrats, the phrase 'but not yet' can be applied to these commitments and in any case they have all back-tracked a little to a position in which only 80 per cent of the House should be elected, leaving 20 per cent to be selected to keep a certain amount of expertise within the House. Some might think that this is a strange position to adopt – it has a certain illogicality. Why do we not need total rather than partial democratic legitimacy? And if we need expertise, why not go for a House full of experts?

Although it has been pointed out many times, at least within the admittedly partisan House of Lords, that we should look first at what we want its function to be and what roles we expect it to play; once these have been agreed we can look at what make-up and structure might best achieve that. But most focus has been on election as a democratically desirable aim without much thought as to what roles we wish to see performed.

Let me come then to why I think an elected second chamber would be a bad thing. First, imagine an elected Lords, with its democratic mandate that will certainly give it greater power and a desire to wield that power on behalf of its electorate. Having been given a mandate by those who have voted for them they will be unable to fulfil that mandate unless they can have a say in legislation. That will immediately put them into potential conflict with the Commons and the end result will be a messy standoff between the two Houses – a recipe for stalemate. It has been thought by advocates of an elected second chamber that, although elected, it would have to be subservient to a House of Commons which would have the final say on legislation, as at present. But to my mind that defeats the object of an elected second chamber. Who would want to vote for a member of such a body if they could not then represent them in parliament and, even more significantly, who would want to put themselves forward for election to such a castrated body? The recent Clegg-inspired bill (Nick Clegg, leader of the Liberal Democrat party) proposed that members of the reformed Lords would be elected for a term of 15 years, at the end of which time they would have to stand down. Here is another strange type of democracy, in which members cannot be thrown out by the electorate if they are not seen to be fulfilling their mandate, and in any case they are out after 15 years. Not much need to consider your democratic legitimacy there then.

It seems that only a minority of existing peers in the Lords would be interested in putting themselves forward for election to such a chamber and it is possible that those who fail to get into the Commons will be the main contenders. A House of failed MPs does not sound like an attractive proposition to me and indeed most of the population at large have expressed zero interest in such a reformed House of Lords. Of the possible compositions of the Lords that achieved most support from the Commons a year or so ago is one in which 20 per cent of peers would remain to be selected rather than elected, in the belief that this would preserve some of the expertise currently residing in the Lords. This again shows a propensity for muddled thinking. If expertise from a wide range of fields is required in the second chamber, why not 100 per cent selected? If democracy is thought to be necessary why not 100 per cent elected? It seems like a fudge with little reason or logic behind it.

The Coalition, Clegg, Bill was withdrawn in the Commons by David Cameron after a back-bench revolt in the Conservative party, much to the chagrin of Nick Clegg and a subsequent threat to the stability of the coalition government. The revolt was led by those who recognised some of the reasoning that I have laid out but more because of the potential threat from a democratically legitimate Lords that would undoubtedly want to wield its responsibilities to its electorate, irrespective of whether the government tried to prevent them doing so. They feared the resulting chaos as the two chambers fought over whose electorate should hold more sway over legislation.

None of the points I have tried to make should be taken to mean that I believe that the House of Lords is perfect and not in need of reform – far from it. Although it does do a remarkable job in many ways and has a range of expertise that would be hard to better anywhere in the world, it has many defects too.

First it is far too large. With over 800 members it is in danger of collapsing under the weight of bodies teeming through its corridors and crowding its chamber. Its numbers should be reduced radically, leaving no more than half that number. It could do that by a variety of means including retirement for those who attend infrequently or fail to contribute, as suggested in the bill put before parliament by David Steel. It is hard too to justify the continuation of the inherited principle for the 90 hereditary members currently in the Lords. To my mind they should slowly be allowed to fall out by natural selection and not be replaced by their heirs or by other 'hereditaries' when they do so. This latter element of the Steel Bill was thrown out in the Lords by a threat of a filibuster by the hereditary peers, but I believe we should bring it back by one means or another.

I also believe that it is unnatural to expect life members of the House of Lords to remain *in situ* for life. In no other spheres is there a possibility of a job for life and it seems reasonable to me to place a time limit of, say, 10 or 15 years on membership. Those opposed to this idea may play on the idea that we are such wonderful people with enormous collective wisdom that we are hard to beat. We should not be jeopardising that by eliminating such wonderful contributors after an arbitrary length of time. I, on the other hand, have never been of the opinion that none of us is irreplaceable and believe that there are very many out there in the wider world who could do as good, if not better, a job if given the chance. All wisdom does not reside solely in the current peerage.

Some have suggested that an age limit, say 75 or 80 years, might be better than a time limit as a way of limiting membership and encouraging turnover. I am less attracted to that idea for two reasons. First, young peers in their 40s may be required to sit for 30 or 40 years and that does not seem equitable. Furthermore if some think that 75-year-old peers are incapable of contributing much to our deliberations and should not therefore be expected to stay beyond that age, they should listen to some of our debates in which the sharp minds of a number of octogenarians continue to be displayed in spellbinding splendour. So a time limit is infinitely preferable to an age limit to my mind.

Another vital element of a reformed House concerns the nature of the selection process. Despite a long history there is now no longer any room for the sorts of patronage that have bedevilled the selection process and caused such recent outrage as the 'cash for peerage' debacle. A process that is open and transparent and one in which the criteria to be adopted for selection are clearly known is the way to go. Included in the criteria one can imagine a series of characteristics that would result in a chamber comprising members from all regions of the UK, a variety of backgrounds, including race and gender, to reflect the general population, and a range of expertise from all the professions, from business, industry, trade unions, local authorities, the arts and academia. Expertise from all these backgrounds as well as from politics could be brought together, after selection, into a reformed and representative House of Lords. Such a chamber might be thought to have sufficient legitimacy to satisfy the most ardent democrat. And it could still function as a revising and advisory chamber that does not itself make the laws but assists the Commons in fulfilling its democratic responsibility.

That is the sort of House of Lords that I would like to see. I am not, however, going to hold my breath.

Chapter 5 The NHS: a suitable case for treatment

A few hard facts

The British economy is in a parlous state with signs that we will be unable to afford any increases in funding for the NHS for several years. Indeed the Office for Budget Responsibility (2012) predicts that the proportion of gross domestic product (GDP) spent on healthcare will fall from about 8 per cent to 7 per cent by 2016, against a background in which the GDP itself fell by 5 per cent between 2007 and 2012. Second, population demographics predict increasing numbers of older people who will make increasing demands on the healthcare system. People now tend to live with their diseases where once they died from them, creating the seemingly counterintuitive observation that the number of deaths has fallen each year since the 1980s. Third, funding for care in the community that many elderly people need is even more sorely stretched than that in the NHS. This accounts in part for the high bed occupancy in acute hospitals that sees 2 million emergency admissions of over 65-year-olds per annum, 10 per cent of whom stay for over two weeks.[14] Many of them would be much better off cared for at home or in some form of longer-term care home than in an acute hospital, but in the absence of community services the hospital is often the only alternative.

It has been calculated that the number of over 65-year-olds will rise by 24 per cent by 2021 and the number of over 85-year-olds by 39 per cent.[15] By 2030 the number of over 85-year-olds will have doubled. Life expectancy is increasing in a linear fashion and a child born in 2011 will live, on average, until he is 93.75 years old or she is 96.7.[16] In a remarkable projection it has been suggested that 50 per cent of those born in 2007 will reach 103 years of age (Filkin report, p 20).[17] By 2015 there will be 5.4 million over 75-year-olds and by 2035 the number will have risen to 8.8 million (Filkin report, p 57).[17] It is fortunate that the length of time spent in non-dependent good health appears to be increasing too so the time spent in dependency is not increasing for women and only modestly for men.[18] However, the demand that this large increase in the number of elderly people will place on health and social services will be severe. Currently, of patients admitted as an emergency to hospital, some two-thirds are over 65 years of age and at any one time they occupy almost 50 per cent of all acute hospital beds (51,000 of 107,000).[19] It is projected that about two-thirds of the over 65-year-olds will require some form of social care (Filkin report, p 57).[17] The figures for the prevalence of dementia in the community are frightening. Currently there are 670,000 patients with dementia and this figure will increase to 1 million within 10 years; about a third of over 85-year-olds will develop dementia by 2036.[19]

It is inevitable that the costs of hospital, and especially community, care will rise. The NHS is projected to see a shortfall of about £54 billion per annum by 2021 on current expenditure levels or, in the unlikely event that it will be capable of continuing to make efficiency savings of 4 per cent every year until then, a shortfall of £34 billion a year will result.[20] Social care shortfalls are even more dramatic in proportion to their much lower funding level. Shortfalls are set to rise from £9.4 billion to £12.7 billion a year by 2022.[21] Overall it has been estimated that total spending for long-term care of older people, both private and public, will have to double in real terms by 2030.[22] A thorough analysis of the current and projected problems in funding for health and social care is set out in devastating detail in the Filkin report (p 20).[17]

Of course, the UK is scarcely alone in having to face up to the problem of increasing demand with limited resources, but here there are many indicators that we are beginning to fail as predictions of a financial cliff edge loom in 2015.

Scarcely a week goes by when there is not a report in the media of yet another disaster in the health service. A GP has missed a diagnosis and a patient has died. A hospital has abused a patient and they have suffered from neglect. Such terrible events seem even more tragic when they are shown to have been avoidable as were the disastrous failures of care at the Mid-Staffordshire Hospital described so clearly in the Francis report of 2013.[23] These scandals are almost always followed by calls for rapid action to prevent them happening again but they are not often judged against a background in which huge numbers of patients are treated perfectly satisfactorily every day. Reaching a judgement on the safety or otherwise of the health service on the basis of high-profile failures is not straightforward, especially when the denominator, that is the total number of patients being treated, is not included in the assessments. When judged in this way one finds that surveys of patient-satisfaction levels show them to be high.

Other indicators give a less rosy picture, however. Comparisons of success rates for the treatment of a number of serious diseases, such as cancers and heart diseases, suggest that the UK lags behind other European countries.[24]

Although survival rates are improving here they are doing so at a slower pace than elsewhere. Furthermore. it is unclear as yet how common the failures in Mid-Staffordshire are in other hospitals. Reports over the years suggest that they are too common for comfort.

Stresses and strains

The government's response to such events is to set up stiffer regulation and more bodies to oversee them. Unfortunately, these examples of poor standards and adverse events are symptomatic of more fundamental defects in the NHS, and a continuing underfunding has played an important part. A disproportionate impact has been felt on the services for mentally ill individuals and for those patients with multiple long-term illnesses, especially in elderly people.

While I enlarge later on these failures and the reasons behind them, I also discuss some of the successes of the NHS, of which there have also been many. First, however, I describe the all too frequent government reforms of the structure and management of the NHS that seem mostly irrelevant to meeting its needs.

Reorganisation and re-reorganisation: a recipe for failure

It is not sufficient that the state of affairs which we seek to promote should be better than the state of affairs which preceded it; it must be sufficiently better to make up for the evils of the transition. (Keynes, quoted in Judt, p 153.[25])

It seems that whenever a new fresh-faced secretary of state for health is appointed he or she finds it impossible to resist the urge to reform the way in which the NHS is managed, organised or run. Each embarks on yet another managerial revolution despite the fact that shifts in management rarely result in improvements that are discernable to patients when all the dust and turmoil have settled. The idea of incremental, as against revolutionary, change does not seem to enter the minds of ministers intent on making their mark before moving on to another department of state in the next shuffle. This, despite the fact that 'health' is often regarded as a graveyard for politicians and many a minister has disappeared without much trace after a period in this department. The latest victim of this syndrome, in 2012, has been Andrew Lansley, dismissed from health to become leader of the House of Commons, an important role, but one without departmental responsibility. It is interesting to read Nick Timmins' devastating critique of the machinations within government as Lansley tried to get his controversial bill past his sceptical colleagues even before it emerged into the public arena.[26] In spite of the history new ministers seem to be mesmerised by a need to change the structure of the service without paying too much attention to changes in its function or whether it is possible to implement their ideas.

During my time in the Lords I have seen so many health bills and acts that I have almost lost count. I reckon there have been at least eight of these and several other health-related bills. They include:

• The Care Standards Act 2000
• Health and Social Care (Community Health and Standards) Act 2001–2
• Health (Wales) Act 2002–3
• Health Act 2005–6
• Local Government and Public Involvement in Health Act 2006–7
• Health and Social Care Act 2007–8
• Health Act 2008–9
• Personal Care at Home Act 2009–10
• Health and Social Care Act 2010–12.

I have spoken in debates on all of these bills at one time or another and raised amendments to most. All the bills have been changed, usually for the better, during their passage through the Lords but, despite all this effort, the final result has too often been found wanting in one way or another. The next secretary of state then feels obliged to introduce yet another bill to try to get round the problems revealed in practice.

At times it seems that only the names of the tiers of management are changed to give the appearance of progress. It is not as if this trend to increasingly frequent ministerially inspired reforms has gone unremarked. Many distinguished observers of the health service have voiced strong views about the futility of repeated structural reform and the damage that is sometimes caused.[27–29]

There are undoubtedly considerable problems faced by any government trying to fund the majority of a nation's healthcare and the economic issues have been well rehearsed. The public is increasingly demanding and is living longer. The proportion of elderly people, whose health needs increase with age, is rising, so that a smaller percentage of the population is faced with funding an increasing load. Furthermore, as more treatments, usually more expensive treatments, become available and more innovative techniques for investigation are discovered, costs rise at a much greater rate than general inflation. These factors present governments with a seemingly impossible task.[30] Most countries across

Europe and the Americas seem to be constantly trying to develop methods of funding that square the circle of providing healthcare on a limited budget. The multiplicity of funding mechanisms testifies to the inadequacies of currently available systems for paying for healthcare.[31]

Leaving aside for the moment the payment system used, there are three theoretical ways by which governments might try to solve the problem. First, simply put more money in, that is give it a higher priority and a bigger slice of the GDP. Second, ration the care provided by the state, that is provide only some sorts of care and not others, or more indirectly by maintaining waiting lists. Third, by being more efficient, that is provide more care for less. This presupposes that private self-funding is not to be a major source, something that is always on the horizon in some governments' thinking.

Historically British governments have been reluctant to go along the route of putting more money in while they have not been satisfied that the possibility of greater efficiency has been exhausted.

The rationale behind government's frequent calls for 'efficiency savings' is hard to deny by anyone with experience of working in the NHS. It is particularly so when the finger is pointed at streamlining 'administration' and using the savings for 'front-line' services. However, reality too often leaves holes in patient care because the level of overall funding in the UK is set at a value that is low compared with most other Western societies. There are inevitable inefficiencies in the NHS but, in trying too hard to remove them all, the 'pips' are made to squeak too loudly.

I come later to the remarkable result when the government resorted to the first of the three options for tackling the cost problem, that is increasing the level of funding. However, in the current economic climate facing the UK, we are more likely to see reductions than increases in funding for the foreseeable future but we should, nevertheless, press for greater priority to be given to healthcare.

Although I start here by discussing managerial structures I focus later on the provision and delivery of care that have a greater chance of improving outcomes and seem to me to be more important than structural reforms.

Chapter 6 **A brief history of NHS reforms**

Many years ago, when I reluctantly first took any interest in managerial structures we had regional health authorities (RHAs), in 14 regions (later reduced to 8), 150 or so district health authorities (DHAs), closer to the ground, and a few hospital boards of teaching hospitals (later removed). As a young professor, in 1973, I was made a member of a hospital board, then a DHA, and shortly thereafter of an area health authority (AHA). The name changes did not make a vast difference. Later, still, I was made a member of the RHA.

This basic structure worked reasonably well in some parts of the country and less well in others. The variability was due largely to variation in the quality and personalities of the managers and abilities of board members, and rarely to structural defects. An RHA covering a population of about 5 million could take a strategic overview of the health needs of that number of people in a way that central government, with a population of 50 million, could not. An RHA could also make decisions about the most rational distribution of hospitals across its region and could ensure that highly specialised services, for example for rare diseases affecting fewer than 1 in 100,000 people, were provided in a limited number of places distributed across its patch. DHAs or AHAs were in a much better position to oversee the local provision of services and were answerable to a local population with local authority membership to ensure that it did. That, at least, was its rationale despite the fact that many in the service were unhappy with 'the managers'. Yet there is much merit in such a basic structure and any dissatisfaction was probably more to do with limited resources than with the way in which the service was organised.

I have laboured over describing this arrangement because it is one that has been made and unmade several times and in several guises over the years since then. It is, however, sobering to note that despite numerous efficiency drives, administrative costs, consuming 5 per cent of the NHS budget before 1997, rose to about 12 per cent after that year.[32]

A major, far-reaching change was, however, the move in 1984 by Ken Clarke, Mrs Thatcher's secretary of state for health, to split the 'purchasers' and 'providers' of healthcare to create an 'internal market'. Hitherto all funding came from the centre and it was difficult if not impossible to exert any control over expenditure. Those shouting loudest received most cash. The new 'market' was supposed to make health authorities, which were given budgets to commission care from hospitals, more cost conscious and efficient. This remarkable introduction of a more business-like system has been continued under successive governments, whether Labour or Conservative, and none has seen fit to change that basic arrangement. However, the fact that we have had a number of unsuccessful attempts to improve this commissioning model over the years suggests that there may be a basic fault with this process.

It is interesting to see how poor an internal market it has turned out to be in practice and I come to that in a moment. Tony Judt, in his inimical style, points out that: 'Markets do not automatically generate trust, co-operation or collective action for the common good' (p 38).[25]

Of course the introduction of a market did not deter any of Clarke's successors from continuing to fiddle with the structure and over the many years since then we have seen repeated iterations in the guise of new bills.

It is interesting, for example, to compare the proposals coming out of the new Health and Social Care Act 2012 with earlier reforms. If they seem familiar, it is because they are. The aim enunciated in the build-up to the 2012 bill was to devolve responsibility for commissioning care to professionals in the field, largely GPs, put patients at the centre of the health system and take day-to-day management of the service out of central government control. These aims seem reasonable and indeed they sound remarkably similar to those laid out in a number of previous bills apart, that is, from a greater emphasis on opening up the NHS to private providers of services. This development of a much greater emphasis on private provision of services to the NHS has raised many concerns but it is only when one comes to examine the details that the difficulties become clear.

Only the names have been changed

Most of the 'innovations' in the 2012 act have turned out to be replicas of earlier health acts. For example, the NHS Commissioning Board (rapidly renamed NHS England for not very obvious reasons), designed to try to distance the management of the health service from central government, has many features of similar but defunct earlier incarnations. The short-lived Health Service Supervisory Board and the NHS Management Board of the 1980s were succeeded by the NHS Management Executive of the 1990s. In a familiar sounding effort to give the Management Board a degree of independence, a businessman was appointed as its first chairman. Ominously for the recent appointment of an independent chair to NHS England, the chairman of the Management Board was soon replaced by a Department of Health minister. It is difficult to escape the impression that ministers over the years have been reluctant to release control while at the same time wanting to keep the service at arm's length. The Department's effort to oversee the Management Board in 1998 by setting up an NHS policy board chaired by the secretary of state was another interesting demonstration of their ambivalence about ceding responsibility to another body.

Simply judged against this background, yet another attempt to devolve responsibility by forming a commissioning board (NHS England) may seem ambitious. The appointment of David Nicholson, a powerful and effective chief executive of the NHS within the Department of Health, as the first chief executive of the new body sets up an interesting power play between him and the secretary of state that may prove tricky. He has had his own problems and will be standing down in 2014 but his successor will undoubtedly want to make his or her own mark and demonstrate the independence of the board. There is also the issue of whether devolving responsibility for the budget of the NHS to a powerful central body, albeit not a government department, will achieve the government's aspiration to devolve responsibility still further to the professionals in the field.

We now have a situation with two sets of potential tension: between the secretary of state and NHS England, on the one hand, and the latter and the widely distributed clinical commissioning groups (CCGs) in the field, on the other. (See Figures 2a and 2b for a picture of the complex structure that has now been set up.)

None of this should be taken to imply that taking the day-to-day management of the NHS out of direct government control is not a valuable objective. It is vital, but there is an unfortunate political expediency which, too often, interferes with its full implementation. Clearly in any state-funded system it is important to have the best overall structure to support the service, but there is always a tension between a need for responsibility for managing and providing care to be as independent of government as possible and at the same time being accountable to government for those functions. It is extremely difficult to avoid the need for parliamentary accountability for the NHS, making a clear line between ministers and management difficult to define. However, Glasby and his colleagues, in a useful contribution, have described the conditions under which it may be possible to distance central government from direct management of the service.[33] It remains to be seen if any government will be open to such advice.

Devolution to local medical budget holding and commissioning bodies, another plank of the new act, also seems vaguely familiar. One might be forgiven for feeling that the new CCGs are not very dissimilar from the GP

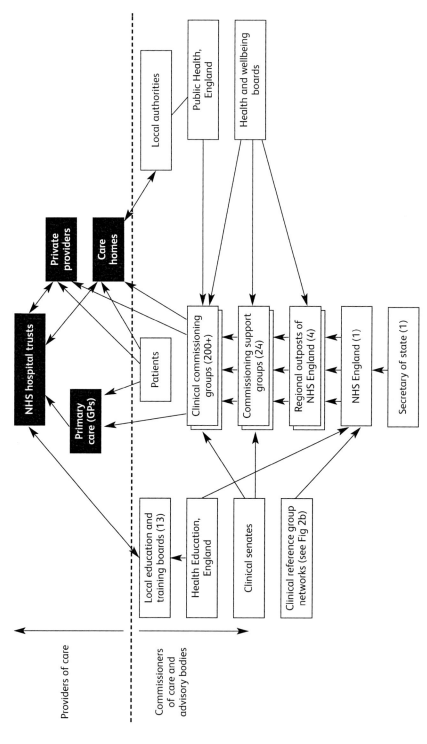

Figure 2a Overview of NHS structures in 2013.

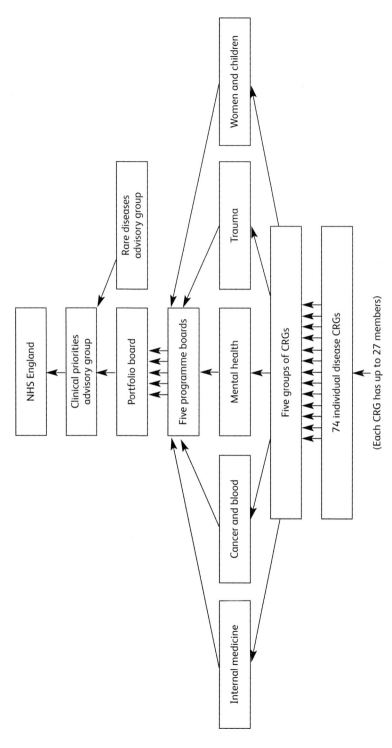

Figure 2b Governance of clinical reference groups (CRGs): How advice about what services should be commissioned reaches NHS England.

budget holders or fund holders of the 1990s, the introduction of which was equally opposed by many GPs then, as in 2012.

Multi-funds were formed later by several practices coming together to perform similar commissioning roles but were lost under a Labour government when primary care trusts (PCTs) were set up. It soon became clear that these too were only variably effective, almost certainly because there were just too many of them. The problem was how to find enough high-quality, able managers to staff all 150 PCTs. Some were very good, others less so. The PCTs in turn have been abolished in the 2012 act to be replaced by the CCGs, which are, astonishingly, to be found in even greater numbers, some 211, than the PCTs. A rapid reappraisal of the practicalities of what such a wide dispersion of budgetary responsibility and management might mean for efficiency has resulted in an amalgamation into a smaller number of larger groupings. It remains to be seen where the final number will fall but lessons from elsewhere suggest that commissioning bodies have to be sufficiently large to be effective.[34]

There have been yet other bodies set up that muddy the water still further. Four regional outposts of NHS England have been instituted, each with a regional director and local offices to ensure that the board can keep a close eye on how the CCGs are going about their commissioning role. In addition, some 24 commissioning support groups are now in place with the important responsibility of not only providing CCGs with all the administrative support that they will need to perform effectively but also holding the contracts for the care that they commission. Figures 2a and 2b give an outline of this increasingly complex administrative structure.

We now have a system in which there is much more central control exerted from the board of NHS England via the outposts and support groups than hitherto and CCGs may well feel somewhat sidelined. This may not be a bad thing because most of the 211 CCGs seem ill prepared to take on the responsibility for such a large part of the NHS budget, somewhere between £60 billion and £80 billion. One might be forgiven for thinking that we are back almost where we started with only very modest modifications to the PCTs that were so roundly criticised. It is, perhaps, helpful that there are only 24 commissioning support groups, aka PCTs, so that they have a much better chance of proving effective than the 150 or so original PCTs.

It is hard to escape the conclusion that we could have saved very large sums of money and much frustration if we would have stuck with the original model and simply adjusted it in the light of experience. It has been said that, among the reasons that Mr Lansley felt there was a need to introduce yet another bill, was the enshrinement in legislation of a much more commercial bias by opening up more opportunities for private providers of services. If this is the case it has been an expensive and disruptive exercise for rather poor and potentially dangerous gains.

It has always seemed necessary to have a body overseeing services for a population of about 5 or 6 million. The original eight RHAs, in round 1, were replaced by the eight regional offices of the NHS Executive in 1996 – round 2. These were found to be ineffective when any budgetary responsibility was taken away from them and they were replaced by 30 strategic health authorities (SHAs), which were soon reduced to 10 – round 3. Although these were clearly distributed regionally, the word 'region' was outlawed by the then Labour government, presumably to avoid confusion with any previous regionally distributed bodies.

Naturally these SHAs have now been abolished under the new regime, revealing a gap that had to be filled. Here we have the four regional outposts or teams (each with a variable number of area teams) and the 24 support groups as described above, but we also have a number of bodies for which the functions are, as yet, ill defined. They include the clinical senates and the clinical networks, which are likely to be advisory in function but all of which need servicing. It remains to be seen what this will mean for numbers of administrative staff.

It seems clear from this unhappy picture that we have been through a cyclical process characterised by periodic calls for reform, followed by incompetent and rushed implementation prompting yet further reform. It is salutary to recognise that the health service introduced in 1948 lasted 25 years before the 1973 reforms, and these in turn lasted several years whereas later reforms have lasted barely two years each. It is noteworthy that the first two acts took several years of planning whereas more recent reforms have usually been introduced with little consultation and commonly against opposition.

Chapter 7 Money talks

The fact that there have been so many attempts to reform the health service says something about a basic defect that has remained stubbornly refractive. The NHS has a history of long waiting lists and patients complaining about the failures of a far from comprehensive service. But there was a step change when a Labour government under Tony Blair decided to increase the funding of the NHS to bring it up to a level similar to the average across the EU. This dramatic shift was announced on the hoof in a TV interview, apparently to the chagrin of the 'prudent' chancellor, Gordon Brown. Suddenly it was realised that, no matter what organisational arrangement the latest reform entailed, when the service is markedly underfunded it will always fail. This unremarkable conclusion had been clearly spelt out in the Wanless report,[35] and was, for once, taken seriously by a Labour government and largely adopted.

Money talks, and what it said was waiting lists will disappear, appointments to see a GP will be available on the same day and patient satisfaction levels will rise. And so they did.

Of course that did not stop ministers from wanting more structural reforms and there were no less than six new health bills in 11 years under the same Labour government, and none of these made anything like the sort of changes perceptible to patients that the increased funding managed to make. Nor was it possible to discern much improvement in efficiency despite the bills.

The most common reason given for the apparent need for further structural reform was that the NHS was in crisis and the experience of throwing money at it was clearly not working. It was said that the large increase in funding that had been poured in had gone into a black hole with no perceptible improvements in patient care.

It was hardly surprising that these views were expressed by opposition parties and the media, but they were clearly erroneous and a review of what actually happened to the extra money and its effects on patient care revealed a different picture.[37]

Investment in the NHS had risen by 6.7 per cent per annum in 1999–2000 and by 9.4 per cent per annum in the years 2001–4 and, by 2013, reached over £100 billion per annum. It now takes 8.2 per cent of the GDP compared with around 6 per cent before 1999.

During the rapid, catch-up phase, some 14 per cent of the rise went on increased salaries but the majority, about 70 per cent, went on increases in the number of staff with about 130,000 more employees, largely clinical, being appointed.[36] By any standard this rate of increase is large and one that had not been seen before, nor is it likely to be seen again.

The question was whether this investment resulted in better care – always difficult to measure but a number of proxies suggest that valuable gains were made. Waiting lists largely disappeared in a comparatively short time. Waits for GP appointments became short, the same day for most and within two days for virtually all. Many of the specialty-specific targets, for cancer and heart disease, for example, were achieved. In April 2004 there were 3,000 patients waiting for three months or longer for angioplasty or coronary artery bypass grafting. By April 2005 no patient waited despite a rise in the number of patients requiring these treatments. The rates for early thrombolytic therapy for coronary artery disease suddenly became the best in Europe, having lagged behind for some years. Times spent in accident and emergency departments, so-called 'trolley waits', came down to less than the target of four hours in most places. So it seemed that the extra staff had been doing something and furthermore every poll of patient opinion revealed a large measure of satisfaction with the service.

It is often assumed that, in trying to provide all the health services that a population needs, a country could rapidly bankrupt itself. Health, or rather sickness, care is a bottomless pit that can never be satisfied. The American experience may be cited in favour of that argument, where even 18 per cent of their much larger GDP seems unable to provide basic care for a large section of society. However, that example cannot be taken at face value and the problem there is caused more by a mixture of maldistribution away from some people, combined with excessive, often unnecessary, provision of investigation and treatment for others, rather than inadequate funding.[37] This is the unhappy position with which President Obama struggled, largely unsuccessfully.

There are other reasons why the argument is faulty. It seems entirely possible to provide a service that the vast majority of the population would find satisfactory for a finite amount of money. That is the case in many countries even though their governments may complain about the costs. It is sometimes said that governments around the world admire the NHS. This is true, but what they admire is the way that we have kept costs down and few seem to be in awe of the quality of our service. In Germany, France, Israel, Sweden and many other countries, patients are largely happy with the services that they receive despite widely different systems for the funding of those services and despite the not infrequent outbreaks of disquiet in their medical professions. But, whatever the funding arrangement, it follows that currently it is possible to provide most of a population's health needs to a satisfactory level within a total input of around 9–10 per cent of the GDP.

The bottomless-pit argument does not hold much water if a 'satisfactory' level of care is defined as one that most rational and reasonable people are pleased to accept. The bottomless pit looms only if every possible 'want' of a population, including the unnecessary, rather than the 'need' is to be met.

It must be the case, too, that, the wealthier a country is, the greater the proportion of its GDP it can afford to use for healthcare, given the political will.

Someone earning £25,000 may be able to afford only 5 per cent of his or her income on healthcare whereas an individual earning £100,000 a year could afford, if he or she wishes, 10 per cent of his or her income. Our own British experiment in moving spending up to 8 per cent or more of our GDP saw a remarkable improvement in care for patients. The American economy as a whole does not seem to have suffered while healthcare costs have mushroomed.

The relationship between funding and level of care has been demonstrated again as the 'Nicholson challenge' has started to bite. David Nicholson, then chief executive officer of the NHS, issued a challenge to the service to find 4 per cent of 'efficiency savings' in each of the five years starting in 2010. The impact of these falls in funding is being felt in 2014 as waiting lists rise again.

The relationship between funding and a satisfactory level of care for the population is clear in a way that repeated reforms of the management of the service cannot match. Although a rate of 9 per cent of the GDP does not seem to be too far out at the moment, it is possible that this will change as the GDP rises and the march of medical science makes more (and more expensive) treatments available. Unfortunately, any suggestion that governments should increase spending on health, or indeed anything else, at a time of economic despondency will fall on deaf ears and the next few years will see particularly sharp stringencies in spending.

Funding is, of course, simply a proxy for that which it purchases and, in particular, front-line clinical staff, the doctors and nurses. Brian Jarman, a number of years ago, neatly demonstrated an indirect relationship between the number of doctors in a hospital and that hospital's mortality rate: the more doctors, the lower the death rate. He also demonstrated that the more GPs the lower the mortality rate in a given population.[38,39]

It remains the case that the number of hospital beds and number of doctors per head of population in the UK lag behind the average for the Organisation for Economic Co-operation and Development countries.

None of this means that there are no problems with the NHS apart from lack of money. This would be quite untrue and I come to some of those problems shortly. Nor should efforts to improve efficiency be decried; indeed they are essential. But it is clear that providing sufficient funds for the service is a much more potent force than repeated expensive efforts to reform its structure.

Change is indeed necessary but it is change in function that is required whereas more structural changes should be strongly resisted.

Chapter 8 More problems with the NHS

Private finance initiative

The delivery of health bills is often frustrated by other in-built difficulties in the NHS.

During the dying days of the Conservative government in 1995–6 Steven Dorrell, then secretary of state for health, embraced a private finance initiative for the health service. This entailed the use of private sources of funding for capital projects, especially new hospitals. The costs were to be paid back over many years, plus interest at a favourable rate to the funder, together with contracts for services to be provided, long term, by those funders. A good deal as far as the funders were concerned but rather less so for the NHS, which has been left with a very long-term and punitive payback regime placing a millstone round the necks of many a trust. It has led to some recent examples of loss of liability, in other words bankruptcy. Six trusts have found themselves in need of rescue in the shape of national financial support. The private finance initiative did, however, allow the building of a large number of much appreciated new hospitals. And it did take the costs of building off the immediate balance sheet, giving the superficial impression of being a good deal for the accountants in the NHS.

Surprisingly, when a Labour government came in, in 1997, they too embraced this tactic and Frank Dobson, the new secretary of state, said that 'it was the only show in town' to get a building programme moving in the absence of ready cash. Under no circumstances can it be judged a long-term outright winner, however.

The unhappy life of a manager

We rely heavily on the local managers of the service to deliver the government's policy of the day. But here we immediately come up against a key limitation on the capacity of the service to deliver. Managers are frequently hamstrung by a plethora of directives from above which rapidly destroy any originality and enthusiasm that they may have. 'Keeping your head down' and 'not rocking the boat' permeate the ethos of the ranks. The net result is that the managers play safe. They tend to find excuses for inaction and avoid ideas that might hint at ways of improving the service. These sorts of jobs, where initiative is frustrated, do not always attract the high calibre of individual whom the service sorely needs. Few on the career ladder seem willing to take on the onerous and often thankless task of chief executive of a trust. The fact that most NHS managers have only been through the NHS graduate scheme, excellent though that may be, and never been in a management job outside the service creates a culture of uniformity. Of course, there are very many highly talented managers working in the service, but my impression is that they are not available everywhere. To spread the pool of talented managers across no fewer than 211 CCGs and over 200 hospital trusts was always going to be expecting too much.

The Department of Health's desire to tightly control the work of those at the coalface can be very counterproductive. It is little wonder then that, whatever NHS reform is proposed on high, it is frustrated by the culture within the service of turgid resistance in those given such reluctant responsibilities. There is a constant pressure, too, to 'balance the books', sometimes to the exclusion of providing high-quality care. In the Mid-Staffs Hospital Trust example it so dominated the management team's thoughts that there was little room for even basic standards of care. Couple that with the fear that any new structural change will inevitably lead to job losses, redundancies and the need to reapply for replacement posts, and you have an insecure workforce and a lack of continuity.

Then there are the difficulties inherent in trying to introduce market forces into a closed system where neither demand nor price is within the control of the managers trying to provide the service. The demand is in the hands of the patients who use the service for free and have no incentive to control their wishes and the price is set on high by the tariff system. No commercial business could manage without having any levers to control demand or price. Furthermore, in a closed system of funding, any move to invest in a new service has opportunity costs, which means that some disinvestment has to occur elsewhere in the service. No investment without the disinvestment is always associated with resistance and pain. The introduction of greater competition among service providers in the 2012 act has distorted this arrangement but it will not make it easier for trust managers.

The development of foundation trusts, with their increased freedoms and many advantages, poses another difficulty for governments wanting to change the ways in which services are provided. The Department of Health finds itself unable to tell hospital trusts how they should behave and central levers for change are now diluted in the rush to devolution. Government may thus be tempted to hide behind the system that has been set up to avoid any action.

Private providers

The coalition government's Health and Social Care Act 2012 included a scarcely veiled attempt to open up the NHS to private providers of services. This was not entirely a novel proposal and under an earlier Conservative government the share of personal services in the private sector had risen from 11 per cent in 1979 to 34 per cent in 1996, mostly in residential care homes (Judt,[25] p 114).

There are, of course, some starkly polarised views about the use of private service providers by the NHS. Some see it as a way to drive up quality and efficiency by the introduction of competition. Others see private providers in the game purely for the profit that they will make from the NHS. I tend to favour the latter view because it seems to me that we are embarking on a process that could undermine the basic principles of the welfare state. We have an NHS for which everyone pays through tax for the common good. It distributes resources to those who need it so that society as a whole can benefit. When the NHS goes down the road of purchasing care from private companies, in competition with NHS providers, we have to be absolutely sure that we have the balance right and that we are getting something worthwhile for society.

In a drive to maximise profits, standards may be allowed to fall with damaging effects for patients and, as Kenneth Veitch has convincingly described, it is eroding social protection as the private sector's objectives shift towards cost saving and profit.[41] Public spending on healthcare rose, on average, by 5 per cent per annum in real terms between 1997 and 2011 and, although spending on private healthcare by individuals fell, spending by the NHS on private care rose to take up some of this fall.[42]

The 2012 act and the subsequent regulations have made it clear that commissioners of services are obliged to go to open tender for all health services unless it is clear that there is only one possible provider. Although this requirement has been in place under previous regulations, driven largely by EU competition law and UK public procurement regulations, it has never been so clearly, or widely, promulgated. The new CCGs are now faced with a potentially large administrative burden if they are forced to comply. They will be regulated in this by Monitor, an organisation recently given new powers to check on whether trusts and commissioners are complying. It is perhaps fortunate that Monitor does not seem to have any appetite to pursue this requirement with any vigour and has given out this message to commissioners. But regulation by a 'nod and a wink' is an insecure way of reassuring the service that competition will not become a disruptive major driver. There are signs even now of competition law inhibiting trusts' ability to make national service re-configurations. Rational mergers of services or hospitals are being frustrated by legal challenges due to CCGs seeking contracts which can be divisive.

However, even with the new pressures in the 2012 bill to increase private sector involvement in the NHS, there were considerable barriers to achieving this. First, after some argument and amendment, private providers are not to be allowed to compete on the grounds of price; prices will be fixed centrally. They will also have to provide opportunities similar to those in the NHS for training and education. And they have to put up with the possibility of a change of government and the insecurity of contracts that this implies. The latter was amply demonstrated when waiting lists in the NHS virtually disappeared after the rapid increase in government funding in the mid-2000s, and suddenly there was less need for the expensive new day surgery centres built by private companies. One American company, Humana, which arrived in the UK with the hope that they would be able to provide the managerial expertise that commissioners of services needed, soon decided that they could not cope with the bureaucratic environment under which the NHS labours. It might appear that only an adventurous private organisation would be willing to take on such trouble and attendant risks. Despite these disincentives, however, there are many private companies willing to enter the market to provide specific, and usually circumscribed, types of service. It remains unclear how far the NHS will go in commissioning services from private providers but the direction of travel is clear and creating resentment within the NHS.

Other types of difficulty have emerged. For example, it is unfortunate that the failure of the government to grasp the opportunity in the Health and Social Care Act 2012 to legislate for mandatory training and registration of healthcare assistants has continued to leave patients in the care of unaccredited and potentially untrained staff. Belatedly there has been a slight weakening of their position, allowing some defined training to be introduced but not registration of trained individuals.

These are some of the systemic problems that permeate the service, making it extremely difficult for a secretary of state to change it from the centre by yet another health bill. It seems to me that it is much more important to focus on these barriers than to dream up yet more brilliant ideas for change. I describe, in a moment, some rather more helpful ideas that could be introduced without touching the structure.

Chapter 9 **A culture of mistrust**

There is another aspect that is worth mentioning.

Whenever a new health bill is announced it is usually accompanied by widespread dismay and resistance by those who have to put it into practice, particularly the health professionals. This is usually portrayed as resistance to change by reactionary doctors wishing to delay progress. However, this explanation is too superficial and far from sufficient. The issues are rather more complex. Nurses and doctors see the problems every day of their working lives and feel frustrated when their concerns are dismissed as 'special interest' or, worse, 'self interest'.

I fear that the resistance stems from a lack of trust that is endemic in the health service. Ministers and civil servants do not trust the doctors or nurses and they in turn certainly do not trust the government. The BMA is seen as a trade union focusing solely on its members and the royal colleges as bastions of privilege. Mistrust is even more widespread, with the managers being suspicious of the doctors and, vice versa, the nurses being unsympathetic to the doctors, and one branch of the medical profession being disdainful of another. Social service departments of local authorities are wary of hospital trusts and the latter are suspicious of the former. Then there are the healthcare workers in allied fields who feel marginalised by everyone else.

This picture may sound something of an exaggeration but it does simmer beneath the surface and it has not been helped by the destruction of the team of professionals that used to be such a cohesive feature of hospital practice as I described earlier (see Chapter 2, p 38).

The most damaging is the sense among health ministers and their civil servants that the doctors are a difficult lot whose views are not to be considered. That doctors can be awkward to manage is hardly deniable. They are individualistic and often intransigent, but that does not excuse the limited consultation with clinicians before ministers announce their bills. This, together with a lack of any hint that proposed reforms might be tested in pilot studies first, inevitably leads to resistance. Although doctors may be seen as reluctant to accept change, it is antipathy to centrally inspired, untested reform that is a greater problem, not resistance to change itself. In practice many successful innovations in healthcare and its delivery come from those in daily contact with patients and not from government. Even though the 2012 act was meant to increase the power and responsibilities of doctors in primary care, as they were centred in CCGs, there was much reluctance among GPs. Some were delighted with being given these responsibilities, but most were not. And of course the influence that they have gained has been considerably diluted by the layers of management, in outposts of NHS England and the support groups overseeing their activities.

A lack of trust manifests itself in a number of ways. There is the large number of regulatory and inspection bodies that have been set up and require all those working in the service to complete innumerable documents to indicate that they are complying, all at great cost and with much duplication of effort. A careful review of this field reported by the Independent Health Care Advisory Service and the NHS Confederation, published in 2009, revealed a total of 35 regulators, auditors, inspectorates and accreditation agencies, which have all of 764 standards with which the service has to comply.[43] Many of these bodies request the same information that several others seek, increasing the burden on those who have to comply. Extra staff have been employed full time to respond to these multiple bodies and it is quite unclear to what use the mass of data generated is put, if indeed it is used for anything (see Appendix 1, p 173 for a list of some of the relevant bodies).

Then there is the daily intrusion into doctors' clinical judgements that should raise concerns for patients, for example the edict, in some places, that prohibits surgeons from following up the patients on whom they have operated on the grounds that GPs could do so more cheaply: economic sense for some minor operations possibly but clinically objectionable for major operations. Patients cannot gain any detailed information about their operation or prognosis while the surgeon is unable to learn anything of the patient's experience.

Some surgeons are no longer making decisions about when they should operate on their patients because operating lists are made up by hospital clerks without their involvement. Little wonder then that they feel that they are being treated as technicians and told to perform at the behest of non-professionals. Other physicians have had their clinic days changed without any consultation, so while the managers despair about resistant consultants, the doctors are frustrated by their dismissive treatment as technicians who must do as they are told. GPs in Camden were expected to give their patients a form to complete confirming that they have been given a choice of hospital to which they have been referred. The forms were then sent for checking by clerks at the primary care trust at a non-trivial cost.

Each of these cases, and I have concrete examples of them all, illustrate some of the ways in which the professionalism of doctors is being eroded with a demoralising effect on them and to the detriment of patients. Of course doctors can be difficult and stubborn as might be expected of highly educated professionals and their trade union, the BMA, has been held up as a bastion of reaction. These characteristics have not endeared them to government or management but it seems to me that this is just the situation in which they need to spend more rather than less time in bringing this body of expert and key deliverers of the service on board. Cursory dismissal of their views is not the best way of engaging productively.

I should say that the hospital in which I spent most of my working life, Hope Hospital in Salford (now renamed Salford Royal Hospital), had, for much of my time there, an enviable reputation for its cohesive spirit of cooperation between clinicians and management. It is now, in 2013, even more cohesive and successful. Indeed it is held up as an exemplar of how NHS trusts should operate in providing an integrated service for the population it serves. They have clearly taken advantage of my absence to make progress. So it is possible to develop a happy working atmosphere, unity of purpose and pride in one's hospital but nowadays this is the exception rather than the rule. Tracing the origins of this damaging deterioration will be important in any service reform.

The difficulty faced by governments of all persuasions is not dreaming up bright ideas about a better future – the world is full of people with bright ideas – but what we singularly lack is those who know how to implement the ideas. And it is implementation that is critically dependent on winning the hearts and minds of those who have to do the implementing, that is the doctors, nurses and managers in the front line facing the patients. When a minister and his or her team feel that they cannot trust the professions, and thus can ignore them, the end result is an unsatisfactory bill that is poorly implemented or, worse, ignored completely. The most successful businesses recognise the value of taking their staff with them but this idea seems to elude governments.

Of course attempting to obtain a national consensus is extremely difficult but it is much easier to get it at a local level and it is here that more effort should be made.

It follows that, in introducing a new system, most effort should be placed in setting the general direction of change while giving as much freedom as possible to those who are being asked to implement it. A sense of trust, ownership and respect for local input can achieve much more than central dictat. Unfortunately government ministers are often in too much of a hurry and, despite recent efforts to devolve budgetary decisions, to GPs this ideal is unlikely to be achieved any time soon.

Chapter 10 Introducing change without pain

Does all my antipathy towards government efforts to reform the NHS mean that I think that the service is beyond criticism? That would fly against all experience and, although there is much to be proud of, there are many defects that make a pressing case for change. But if you were trying to design a healthcare system from scratch you would have to start with the patients. Who are they, where are they, what illnesses do they have or are liable to develop, and what is the nature of their needs? The NHS has collected data on patients and their needs for decades, so it should not be impossible to calculate the likely demand for care nationally and locally. The prevalence of diseases in the community, together with the incidence of new cases, provides an estimate of demand and this, together with the average cost for each type of case, could allow calculation of the overall costs of the service. Such estimates could then be refined for each area of the country with their own specific demands. On this basis the need for services within the community and in hospital might be estimated.

What specific roles do we expect our hospitals to play? If we answer this by assuming that they are designed to provide 'high-tech' investigation and treatment, to deliver acute care for the many emergencies that arrive at their door, both surgical, including trauma, and medical, and to provide specialised care for complicated or rare diseases, then we can gain some idea of how many of them we need, where they are best sited, how many and what type of staff are required, and how many beds are needed. They also need to be designed to take account of the need to provide training, education and research.

In the community, an assessment of patients' needs for long-term care could be made and the demands and costs for social services, GPs and care homes could be estimated. We do have data that could be used in this way, but of course we are not starting from scratch and unfortunately we are nowhere near being able to use such information as a base for service design. Governments may well fear that this type of approach would present them with too large a bill.

Here I briefly review the limited opportunities that are open for us to tackle these difficulties.

Avoiding NHS structural reform

First it is important to avoid repeating the errors of the past, especially keeping clear of more structural reorganisations. Imperfect though the current arrangements may be it will be infinitely better to keep them and try to make them work better than to throw them all up in the air yet again.

Confidence in a government's stewardship of the health service is almost always low and there must be considerable political advantage for a government to distance itself from the direct management of the service. There is a good case then for a body at a national level that is not directly politically driven yet can give government a reasonable level of confidence and the new, 2012, NHS England is a reasonable proposition.

If it works well the government should restrict its own role to developing policy and overall strategy as well as setting the budget. Glasby and colleagues[33] set out very well the roles to which government should restrict itself. NHS England, working within this framework, should be responsible for ensuring that the strategy was being fulfilled, for the equitable distribution of resources between the regions and for certain supraregional activities. It is, of course, extremely difficult for any government to devolve responsibilities completely because whenever there is some disaster somewhere in the service, as there inevitably will be, questions will be asked in parliament and ministers will have to respond. Nevertheless an attempt must be made to move management as far out of the Department of Health as possible.

It is clear that it is almost impossible to manage the care of 50 million people from the centre. Populations of about 5–6 million are much more manageable propositions, as shown in Scotland, and a body given responsibility at this level should be able to fulfil this need. Regional health authorities and strategic health authorities were in this position and in my scheme the regional outposts of NHS England would have to take on this role.

If we are to avoid more disruptive reorganisations we should increase the number of these outposts from four to about eight, and give them responsibility for budgetary control and making rational, transparent decisions about the distribution of hospitals and other services across their regions. In supporting under- and postgraduate education and training, they will need to work closely with their local universities.

It will be essential for them to have access to timely data about their population's needs and to the performance of commissioners and providers. Structure should follow function. Data on populations of a manageable size, indicators of their degree of deprivation and their likely burden of disease are among the most significant information requirements. These data, combined with recommendations on best practice derived from clinicians, the colleges and professional societies should be the basis for the design of services.

High-quality IT and data analysis will be vital. If the difficulties that were faced by PCTs at the local level are not to be duplicated, we should focus responsibilities on a smaller number of CCGs – say 40 or 50 nationally. Experience elsewhere suggests that successful commissioning is dependent on focusing it on a small number of commissioners to avoid spreading scarce resources too thinly.[34] It is also likely to be cheaper.

It is obvious, from this description of a desirable three-tier system using NHS England, about 8 regionally distributed bodies overseeing the care of about 5 or 6 million people (perhaps as outposts of NHS England but with devolved budgets) and the CCGs as I have suggested, that we concentrate on an existing, albeit reformed structure to provide the functions that I believe are needed. These newly named bodies would not, however, function as envisaged in the 2012 act but, rather than more disruptive structural mayhem, their roles could morph into those suggested.

NHS and social care

More significant changes, which have very little to do with managerial structures and tiers, are, however, required if we are to meet the needs of the population. These changes are more concerned with the ways in which care should be provided now and in the future when there are so many indicators that we are failing in too many ways.

We have reached a situation where we have two starkly contrasting standards of care. On the one hand, we have mostly high-quality care much of the time for patients with single episodes of acute illnesses and for specialised care whereas, on the other hand, we have poor and often failing standards of care for the large number of patients with the multiple complicated and long-term illnesses that are so common in elderly people. Report after report has been published bemoaning the poor standards of care given to elderly patients both in hospital and in the community.[23,43–46] We have an NHS designed for care in acute general hospitals while increasingly the need is for longer-term care for elderly people largely in the community. This is not an either/or situation and should not be taken to mean, as it is by some commentators, that we need less acute and specialised care; indeed the demand and need for them are increasing. But we are desperately short of longer-term care in the community and it is little wonder that older people feel that their care is fragmented, underfunded and failing to meet their needs. One might be forgiven for feeling that repeated health bills simply move the deckchairs while the ship is sinking.

I concentrate here on the nature of the problems faced by the health service day to day, how we might meet the needs of the population where they are needed and by whom they will be met, namely the nurses, doctors and carers.

The fact that about a third of acute hospital beds are occupied by patients who should not be there and who would be better off at home has led some to the simple answer: close a number of acute hospitals or wards and transfer the funds released to care in the community. However, this superficially attractive solution is unlikely to meet the needs of the underfunded social services and, for a number of reasons, considerable caution is needed if we are to move far along this route. There may be good reasons for closing some poorly performing hospitals, but closing some simply to provide resources for care in the community is a poor and potentially damaging idea. The reasons why this is so are as follows.

First, most emergency admissions of elderly people are for acute illnesses such as strokes, heart attacks, fractured hips, and so on, which need the attention and expertise focused in acute hospitals. Some of these admissions should be avoidable but few are unnecessary. They need acute care for such episodes even though they may have multiple other confounding chronic disorders.

Second, money saved in ward or hospital closure comes largely from staff reductions because 70 per cent or so of hospital costs are consumed by staff. But currently there are too few nurses and doctors to meet existing demands for acute care. If hospitals were to be closed, staff numbers would be unlikely to fall by much given the greater intensity of acute care that would fall on remaining hospital beds. The workload of acute hospitals is determined less by the number of beds and much more by the rapid turnover of acutely ill patients. It is for this high-intensity work, rather than bed numbers or even the number of long-stay patients, that staff are most needed and where most of the costs arise. This may account for the intriguing observations of Julian Forder who showed that, for every pound spent on community care, less than 30 pence was saved in hospital costs.[47]

It is true too that, although bed numbers have fallen by a third in the last 25 years, acute admissions have risen by a third.[14] Despite a strong lobby to reduce bed numbers even more, it is worth noting that we lag behind the average bed numbers in countries of the Organisation for Economic Co-operation and Development (OECD), at 3.4 per 1,000 of the population, whereas in the UK we have 2.4 per 1,000.[48]

New ways of working, including seven-day consultant cover as proposed by the Academy of Medical Royal Colleges, will increase the need for doctors, and the Royal College of Nursing has emphasised a requirement for more nurses to meet current demands, largely for acute care. Pressure to adhere to at least a minimum number of nurses per patient, following the Francis report, will add to the bill for nurses.

Closure of hospitals without careful thought and calculation of how current and predicted demands for acute care will be met would be very damaging.

Filling the gaps

I have mentioned the rash of reports making predictions about the gap that is looming in funding for long-term care of elderly people. Some have used time frames of 10, 20 and even 50 years into the future, when straight-line extrapolations lead to nightmare scenarios.[22,49,50] Such projections are increasingly shaky the longer their view and, although it is vital to try to make plans based on current information, we have to be prepared to change them radically in the light of developments. Economic projections are notoriously uncertain and social change is unpredictable. Looking back at the medical advances I have seen over the last 50 years, when it would have been impossible to suggest any of the major changes in diagnosis and treatment that have occurred, I recognise the difficulty of predicting future advances that may transform medicine and our lives.

There are, therefore, two problems with which we have to deal and both are urgent. The first is finding solutions for current difficulties and the second is developing plans now for an uncertain future. Both should be tackled without delay.

Keeping elderly people out of hospital

In the short term there are several simple measures that might help elderly people stay at home. If social service departments, together with those in primary care, could formulate registers of those most at risk in their populations, then a focus on the specific needs of these individuals would bear dividends. Attention to housing and aids in the home, as well as regular visits to monitor mood and nutrition, could be invaluable. It may well be that such increased efforts will be more costly to local authorities but would save money for the NHS in reduced admissions. Unless, of course, the hospital service can be persuaded to fund, jointly, these preventive measures as is being trialled in the Inner North West London Integrated Care Pilot. It boils down, inevitably, to funding and its distribution, although it is noteworthy that Salford Royal Hospital Trust has gone some way to resolving the problem, at least in part, by integrating their community and hospital services. They have done so by taking the innovative approach of employing a number of GPs and directly funding and managing care homes for their community.

Attention paid to the particularly vulnerable by GPs in their practices can pay dividends, however. 'Dizzy dos' and falls are common reasons for admission and their prevention could be reduced by such common-sense interventions as better lighting, hand rails, chair lifts and regular home visits to check on nutrition. It is possible to reduce the incidence of fractures, especially the very common hip fractures that have such a big impact on hospital admissions, by reducing the prevalence of osteoporosis. Screening, prophylaxis with calcium and vitamin D, and regular exercise should help. 'Blackouts' are common and screening for predisposing causes, such as cardiac rhythm disorders, transient ischaemic attacks and predisposing causes, including epilepsy and hypertension, can reduce admissions.

All of these measures require the active involvement of GPs and their staff and it is not clear whether they are all geared up to provide this high-level, but common-sense, service. It is clearly something that NHS England, the funder of GP services, should take up.

Shortly I will describe longer-term public health measures that should help keep people healthy for longer.

Improving communication

Although elderly people certainly need acute hospital care, they often linger inappropriately in hospitals for far too long, when they should be at home or in a convalescent or care home. The reasons for delayed discharge include poor communication between hospital and social service staff, but especially the lack of resources available to local authorities. The variable availability of GPs out of hours and at the weekend does not help either.

Of course, none of these reasons for delay excuses the poor standards of care for elderly people in hospital and here again there are multiple causes. I spelt these out in a speech I gave in the Lords in 2011, reproduced in Appendix 2, but here I concentrate on delays in discharge and how they might be overcome.

There is little doubt that, where systems have been developed to integrate services across the hospital/community divide, they have proved invaluable in speeding discharge, reducing length of stay and improving efficiency. Torbay is usually held up as the best example of a trust where integration of hospital and social services works well.[28] Here they have formed a single care trust with a chief executive acting in this capacity across the hospital trust and social services department but there are several other examples around the country.

Torbay has a relatively small population so it may be easier to manage, but elsewhere, where there are larger and more diverse populations, there are different arrangements for close working that are equally successful in the rapid transfer of patients. These include Bradford and Airedale, Norfolk, Cumbria, Hereford, Salford and North West London (Filkin report, p 20).[17] Spreading this type of good practice must be an essential aim for reform and improvement, yet this is not the case in most of the country where there are no systems in place to communicate in a timely way between the two services. As noted in the Filkin report, accountability rules and competition currently limit the capacity for integrated care.

I would like to see the appointment of case managers acting as liaison officers, whose specific role is to arrange the transfer of patients between hospitals and the community. It is another initiative that could bear dividends because case managers could ensure that, from the moment a patient is admitted, a plan is developed for discharge several days later. GPs can be alerted and social service departments given adequate notice so that home visits and support services can be organised in a timely way. This could obviate the last-minute arrangements that almost always cause delays. I am concerned that this simple system, or something like it, is not practised everywhere.

It would be extremely beneficial if it became possible to appoint medical and nursing staff who care for patients both in the community and in hospital. Some limited efforts have been made to secure this type of arrangement, in community paediatrics, for example, and geriatricians in the past spent time seeing patients at home. Liaison nurses have all but disappeared as joint funding mechanisms have fallen victim to funding strictures in social services and the NHS. More effort should now be made to bridge this gap. The continuity of care that this would engender could be invaluable.

'Bundled' contracts

Current contractual arrangements for individual and distinct packages of care also mitigate against full cooperation, but, where specialists, GPs, nurses, other clinicians and patients, working together with the managers, can agree integrated care 'bundles' for different patient categories, a more effective system could be developed. Funding 'bundles' for a 'year of care' would be invaluable in obviating the current splintering of care by multiple contracts. The results of such an agreed arrangement can be fed into contracts involving both the local authority and hospital trust. Best-practice guidance produced by specialist societies, royal colleges or the National Institute for Health and Care Excellence (NICE), for example, tailored to local need should inform this process. This has proved difficult partly from a lack of trust between the parties but more often because of inadequate resources in the community. Pooling NHS and social service budgets could facilitate this integrated care, but simply pooling two inadequate sources of funds is unlikely to be a total solution.

Funding trumps all

Current stringencies have reduced staffing numbers that are now inadequate to meet the needs of patients at home. Home visits lasting 10 or 15 minutes a day, not necessarily every day, are far too short to feed, bathe or chat to an elderly, needy person isolated at home. There are far too few publicly funded convalescent or longer-stay homes for those who cannot manage in their own homes, and private facilities are variable in the standard of care that they provide.

There are few signs that the coalition government in 2014 is willing to contemplate increasing resources for local authorities and the idea that NHS / local authority budgets might be pooled for this purpose, although floated on many occasions, has not been greeted with any enthusiasm by the NHS. It complains of being 'cash strapped' itself and is unwilling to go far along this route; indeed, the Nicholson challenge to make 4 per cent savings each year for five years is biting hard without having to contemplate hiving off even more funds.

However, the idea of pooling NHS and social services budgets for care of elderly people in order to lower boundaries is certainly attractive and was put forward in 2013 by Andy Burnham, Labour's shadow health secretary, in his proposals for a future NHS. Although pooling two inadequate sources of funding does not sound like a full answer, it is, nevertheless, worth pursuing for other reasons. The practical 'pooling' of services at Salford Royal Hospital Trust has achieved some of this and, as a result, they have managed to close some 170 beds.

Although there is emphasis in the NHS mandate to NHS England on 'integrated care' and the secretary of state in 2012 has made the improvement in care for elderly people one of his key objectives, in the absence of funds it is difficult to know how these aspirations will be translated into action across the service.

Recent reports have also focused on the huge gaps in services for mentally ill individuals.[51] Mental illnesses are said to account for 40 per cent of all diseases and they have a major impact on morbidity and mortality.[52] Yet services for mentally ill individuals are poorly resourced and, relative to the rest of the NHS, it remains a Cinderella service. There are gaps in GP training; some 40 per cent have received no training in mental health and there is a severe shortage of psychiatrists. There is a wide discrepancy between the existence of effective therapies and their availability, including such straightforward, non-'hi-tech' treatments as cognitive–behavioural therapy which has been shown to be economically as well as therapeutically beneficial.

Hospital 'rationalisation'

The arguments outlined above about the unreliability of the release of funds by hospital closures should not be taken to mean that rationalisation of hospital services is not desirable for other reasons. It is, for example, undoubtedly the case that there are gains to be made in better and more effective treatment of serious diseases by concentrating the necessary expertise and infrastructure in fewer centres of excellence. The example of stroke services is a valuable one where patients have benefitted from early rapid access to the best treatment possible in a smaller number of centres. The medical royal colleges are pressing hard for similar rationalisation of other specialised services.

However, closing wards or hospitals with the aim simply of providing funds to transfer to community care is an unrealistic proposition. Furthermore, reducing general acute services in advance of adequate services in the community could be disastrous. Where would the patients go? The provision by government of a 'bridging loan' would help build up community services before bed closures which might then follow rather than precede community facilities.

'Efficiency gains' are clearly there to be made but I have considerable doubts whether they will be sufficient to fund enough of the care in the community that is needed, at least not on top of the current 'Nicholson' targets of 4 per cent savings per annum for the NHS.

Facing the long term

There are some solutions on which more faith than reality may be placed. Improvements in lifestyle can undoubtedly reduce the incidence of many diseases. Better public health through smoking cessation, reduction in obesity and alcohol consumption, and more exercise will increase healthy life expectancy. Improved housing and better screening will be helpful too. But these measures offer only very long-term solutions and, even if those sections of the public currently resistant to such messages were to take them up, there would not be a payback for some years to come. We have to press forward with these messages but cannot wait for them to be fully effective in reducing the burden of disease.

Other ways of preventing illness are helpful but again they take some years for their benefits to come through. Prevention of hip fractures by measures to reduce osteoporosis and strategies to reduce falls in elderly people are certainly valuable, and the prevention of heart attacks and strokes by better control of blood pressure and cholesterol will be valuable. If current exciting research into new treatments for Alzheimer's disease and other dementias and for a variety of cancers bears fruit, it will transform the demands for health and social services. We might then move into a future in which most people live longer, healthier lives before dying suddenly after a short illness and leaving little need for long-term care. I fear, however, that we should not be holding our breath in waiting for this nirvana to be reached. Experience to date suggests that health and social care costs have never shown a dip in a graph that simply rises year on year as new and more expensive treatments emerge. We should hope for such a future but can hardly rely on it and meanwhile we have to plan on the basis of simple extrapolations from what we already know, fraught with uncertainty though that may be.

The Filkin report of the House of Lords, *Ready for ageing* in 2013, painted a very compelling case for long-term planning (p 20).[17] Governments tend to think and plan in five-year time spans at best and here was a call for a much longer planning time scale. Apart from encouraging governments of all persuasions to begin this planning process urgently, the report summarises the size of the problems and makes a number of valuable recommendations. It gives an estimate of the frightening shortfall in funding by 2030. Where these estimates may be unreliable lies in the incorporation of the costs of caring for predicted rises in the number of people with diabetes, coronary heart disease, stroke and dementia. I am less convinced that we will see such continuing rises because there are signs even now that we may be able to change the course of these diseases over a 10- or 20-year time span. However, this does not detract from the general thrust of the argument that we should be preparing for continuing increases in the needs of elderly people.

Among proposals for meeting the rising costs of care, there seems little alternative to delaying retirement, better pension planning for retirement, encouraging part-time work, and greater attention to the housing needs of old and infirm individuals. There is little evidence that the insurance industry is willing to offer insurance for long-term social care so we will have to fall back on private self-funding for those who can afford it or the state will have to foot the bill.[53]

The Filkin report points to a need for a radical change in the way in which health and social services are delivered but is light on how that might be achieved. There is then a plea to government to seek a cross-party consensus in developing a long-term plan. I could not agree more.

The elephant in the room remains the need to put more money into health and social services. Potential sources of this funding include delaying retirement, pension reform, part-time work, part self pay, and so on, and are simply ways of finding the money that everyone knows is needed. The current and future governments will have to face the problem of defining their funding priorities. If the public were asked, it is likely that, in our democracy, a majority would place a high priority on the way in which we care for our elderly and infirm individuals. Do nuclear submarines or high-speed trains have a higher appeal and should they have a higher priority? This is not simply a question for the Department of Health or the Department of Works and Pensions alone; it is a question that the whole government will have to face. Departments responsible for housing and for transport and, above all, the Treasury have to be involved. We need a minister to take responsibility for a new role in coordinating the cross-departmental activities that are needed and it is now urgent that the government takes a grip.

Trust the professionals

Earlier I described the damaging distrust of doctors and nurses by the government and here I expand on where and how I believe the professions can play a much more positive and effective role in the health service.

Since clinicians have to provide day-to-day care for patients in the NHS it might seem obvious that they should be fully engaged in its design. These highly trained professionals are a precious resource that is currently being underused.

For doctors to become more directly involved in managing the service some at least will need to have more relevant training and education available to them. Recent proposals to develop management educational programmes will help as will greater recognition of management skills in postgraduate education schemes run by the royal colleges.

But the great majority of doctors want to get on with the job for which they have entered medicine, that is to care for their patients. This is what gives them the most satisfaction but currently they are distracted by an overbearing load of administration. For most consultants about 25 per cent of their time is spent in non-clinical work which they view as an inefficient use of their time. It follows then that only a minority of clinicians need to be, and should be, engaged in these important administrative roles. For most it is vital that we reduce the bureaucracy under which they labour.

Currently the Department of Health relies heavily on individual specialist 'czars' and makes too little use of advice from professional bodies such as the specialist societies and royal colleges, which represent a considerable body of untapped expertise. 'Czars' are no doubt knowledgeable but cannot alone provide all the relevant expertise that should be used in helping governments develop their ideas. They themselves also need the support of their peers if they are not to be treated with suspicion. There is an ingrained suspicion, and possibly fear within the Department, of advice given by expert bodies but there is much to be gained by bringing them into the advisory framework and much to be lost by their exclusion.

The professions too are in the best position to spread good practice. There are many valuable innovations in clinical practice that have been introduced by doctors and nurses that both help patients and improve efficiency. But there is little encouragement currently from the NHS, centrally or locally, for these developments to be taken up more generally. Grassroots innovations seem to have less credence than those derived from central government, yet greater involvement of the professions in recommending and spreading good practice would pay considerable dividends. One example illustrates the difficulties. A consultant instigated a phone-in clinic for follow-up patients to avoid their having to make repeated trips to the hospital. This was frowned upon by the trust because it reduced their income from outpatient visits.

Spreading good practice cannot be inflicted by edict from the centre. It has to come from within the professions and be led by them. Giving the professionals a sense of ownership is simply good employment practice.

Towards abolishing bureaucracy

Apart from avoiding more structural reform and concentrating on functional change, there are a number of other activities we should avoid or abolish.

We should, for example, set a bonfire under the large number of inspection and regulatory bodies that exist.[42] Previous efforts to rationalise these were only minimally effective and the remaining ones, over 37, need close examination (a list is given in Appendix 1). Many of these have overlapping functions with considerable duplication of effort needed to respond to them. A careful review of the impact of this multiple array of bodies revealed that almost 60 per cent of the information being sought was of no value to the inspected and not even looked at by the inspectors. A voluntary concordat between regulators instigated by the Healthcare Commission to encourage rationalisation has had no perceptible effect. Problems include excessively wide-ranging questionnaires of little obvious value and the duplication of requests for the same information which all require a heavy investment in time and personnel employed to respond. A detailed investigation is required of the need for each regulatory and inspection body, of their individual sets of information requests and of the necessity for each of their visits. Their cost should be critically evaluated and set against the value of the end result. These costings should include not only the bureaucracy necessary for their operation but also the attributable costs of the time and paper of those who have to respond.

The government's response to the Francis report on the poor standards of care at the Mid-Staffs Hospital, involving yet more regulatory bureaucracy, is heavy-handed and ignores the likelihood that it will not achieve its aims. Punitive action after an adverse event is too late. A better answer lies in prevention by the placement on each ward of someone who is there all the time, namely the nurses. We should have a senior career-grade nurse, an old-style sister, there to oversee what is happening to the patients every day. No one else from outside that environment can do it. When such mature able women (there were few men) were in charge of their wards they knew everything about every patient and would not have countenanced the falls in standards witnessed in Mid-Staffs. It is unfortunate that now nursing sister and charge nurse posts are viewed simply as stepping stones towards a career in teaching or management, and they rarely stay longer than a year or so. My solution is to bring back career sisters or charge nurses to stay on the wards, reward them accordingly, with a salary similar to that of a consultant, and give them the respect they deserve for the vital role they play.

There are the problems too that arise when several centrally inspired changes are introduced at the same time. The room for confusion and conflict between these edicts is considerable. 'Patient choice' seems a reasonable idea at first sight but in practice most patients simply want to be seen quickly at a hospital nearby and by a consultant who is recommended by their GP. Well-informed patients may know, from recommendation or repute, which consultant they would like to see. But 'patient choice' means something else and the choices that patients would like are either not available or in limited supply. Some PCTs operated a system in which GP referral letters were intercepted, read and re-referred to a service of the PCT's 'choice'. Sometimes the letters were sent back to the GP if the PCT's 'clinical assessment treatment service' thought the referral was inappropriate. Contracts with independent treatment centres distorted referrals away from a patient's choice by contractual obligations – what a wasteful and expensive set of regulations causing unnecessary delays and sometimes erroneous referral. The professionalism of the doctors was cast aside by the bureaucratic machine that we had set up. Clearly we must not repeat these mistakes in any future rearrangement of the service.

Reprise

It is pretty clear that we, in the UK, have been unable to take full advantage of our lead in providing universal healthcare, free of charge at the point of service. Despite enormous efforts by governments of all persuasions, and despite a great many reforms of the management of the service, it is operating under an increasing financial strain. The strain is set to become much worse as we are facing a financial 'cliff edge' in 2015. It is usually said that the reasons boil down to the fact that we can ill afford a system in which demands are rising at a much greater rate than we can pay for. Inflation in medical care costs rises much faster than normal, non-medical inflation.

So we have to think of either reducing demand or finding other sources of money, or becoming much more efficient. Each of these has been examined exhaustively without an obvious solution emerging.

We clearly must try to become more efficient. Certainly the problems are compounded by poor management and inefficiency which are so inextricably linked and common. The increasing difficulty of recruiting good managers when many are fearful of the system that they will have to operate under is compounded by having to spread this important resource across too large a number of commissioning bodies. Lack of leadership, poor engagement with and by clinicians, the legacy of the private finance initiative, the disruptions caused by the 2012 reorganisation of the service, coupled with the Nicholson 4 per cent annual savings targets are all contributing to the looming funding crisis. Short-term solutions to the increasing number of failing trusts, such as those undertaken by the Trust Development Authority to parachute in 'turn around teams' with 'failure regimes', offer only temporary patch-ups. With over 30 trusts potentially going into deficit in 2014–15 the size of the problem is becoming increasingly obvious.

At the same time there is an increasing need for more nurses, to bring up the nurse:patient ratios to safe limits and for doctors to provide seven-day availability.

Close hospitals and move the savings made into community is a commonly proposed solution. But the absence of facilities in the community in advance of closures will leave patients much worse off. We need to build up community services and general practice before we start any closures. Filling the gap will need more money. It may be that those funds could come as a temporary measure, a 'bridging fund' to be paid back when, and if, it becomes possible to reduce hospital or bed numbers.

But I fear that the fact remains that, if we are to continue to maintain a health service as a national good, and few in any government will admit to not wishing to do so, it is inevitable that more funds will have to be found to maintain an acceptable level of service. Non-government sources of funds, perhaps through private insurance or personal co-payment, may offer some help but, for all the reasons I have mentioned, these have their own drawbacks. I am drawn to the conclusion that the government of the day will have to bite the bullet and provide a larger slice of the GDP, drawn from taxed income, for health and social care. This is a solution that most governments find unrealistic and unacceptable. The coalition government in 2014 is faced with a combination of poor productivity and a high national debt, and is looking to cut public spending rather than increase it. But the NHS bottomless-pit argument does not bear close examination, as I outlined earlier, and in a country as relatively affluent as ours is not sustainable.

The priority that the voting public gives to health and social care is very high and is likely to be rather higher than many other uses to which government funds are put.

Chapter 11 **Odd-job man**

Ethics and medical practice

I have spoken in the Lords from time to time on ethical issues. Assisted dying or assisted suicide, embryonic stem cell research, research using animals, sperm donation and water fluoridation are among these topics. I reproduce some of my contributions here to give an idea of my views for what they are worth.

Assisted dying

Assisted dying, a consistently high-profile topic, has been discussed several times during my 13-year stint in the Lords. A private member's bill has been introduced at least twice and I had the privilege of sitting on a select committee that examined the issues in depth.

In the debate on Lord Joffe's bill on 12 May 2006, I said:

> *I have thought long and hard since our previous debates on the subject of this Bill but I am sorry to say to the noble Lord, Lord Joffe, for whom I have enormous respect and whose motives I admire, that I cannot support the Bill.*
>
> *I say that not because I am against the principle that we should do all we can as society in general, and as doctors in particular, to relieve patients' suffering, especially the type of heartrending cases that we have heard about today. When they are terminally ill, I'm not against easing their passage from this life as best we can by palliative care; how could I, as an ex-practising physician, not support the principle? All my feelings and emotions are in favour of those who speak for the bill.*
>
> *Nor am I against the bill because of any religious convictions that I may have, because I do not wish to inflict those convictions on others who do not hold them. I am against the bill for entirely practical reasons – the unintended consequences of acceding to one patient's desire for assisted suicide when the risks entailed for others seem, to my mind, to be too great. The probability of a risk to*

the aged, the disabled and the depressed, who may feel a burden to others, despite the safeguards in the bill, seem to me to be too high. The finality of that risk, the termination of a person's life, is too severe. When mistakes are made they will be fatal, and mistakes seem inevitable. Mistakes, such as a wrong diagnosis or a misdiagnosis of depression, will go undetected.

I have tried hard to see whether it would be possible to amend the bill to the extent that my anxieties could be allayed. Perhaps we could better define terminal illness, or change 'unbearable' suffering to 'unrelievable' or 'intractable' suffering. Perhaps we could relieve doctors of the responsibility for assisting in the demise of a patient, as the majority of doctors seem to wish to be relieved, and give it to some other professionals to pursue. But I am afraid that none of these types of amendment would get round my concern and for these reasons I cannot support the bill.

Although I thought that the Joffe bill should be allowed to go on from the second reading to allow more debate, it was prevented from doing so on a vote. Subsequently, however, partly as a result of pressure from advocates of assisted dying and partly because of some high-profile cases, especially the Debbie Purdy case, the director of public prosecution published a set of valuable criteria by which he would judge whether someone who had helped a suffering patient to die should be prosecuted. If it was clear that these criteria were met and if it was not in the public interest to take action then no prosecution would follow.

I thought that this was a useful method of ensuring that someone who helped another to die for impeccable motives would not have to be taken to court while ensuring that the law remained in place to discourage others who may have less altruistic motives.

In a short debate on this topic on 13 February 2012, I said:

The question I ask myself is whether the experience of the public prosecutor leads us to believe that we should now change the law. Fewer than 20 cases a year have been referred to the DPP and none, so far as I am aware, have led to a prosecution. A new law would, in effect, lower the barrier and remove the critical safeguard provided by an independent body making a fair and objective judgement. The question we have to ask ourselves is not whether it is desirable to make it easier for someone with impeccable motives to help a person suffering unbearably to die. They can do that now in the knowledge that the DPP has been shown to act in an entirely appropriate and humane way. The question really is whether a change in the law will make it easier for someone with selfish, ulterior motives to help an elderly, infirm relative to die. A combination of the current law and the DPP provides a safe and humane system that we should jettison to our disadvantage.

It is certain that the last word has not been spoken on assisted dying for terminally ill and suffering patients and another bill will no doubt appear before parliament at some time. I will continue to look critically at the safeguards that will need to be in place if I am to be satisfied. I have to admit that I have stiff opposition to my position on this at home. Edna is firmly in favour of assisted dying, as indeed is Ray Tallis, a good friend whose opinions I fully respect. I suspect that I might have to yield at some point but I will do so only if I am convinced that the safeguards are robust enough to prevent vulnerable people being swept up in a law that is too open to abuse. I am not yet in that position.

Cloning and embryonic stem cell research

If ever there was a topic that provoked strong and opposing views, research using stem cells derived from human embryos is it. It has been the subject of debate in the Lords several times while I have been there and I have been privileged to participate in and to hear some remarkable speeches. The Lords excel in this type of debate and this topic has been no exception. As might be expected, my view was that embryonic stem cells are extremely valuable research tools with considerable potential for cures of diseases that have been difficult to treat. Neurological diseases such as Parkinson's disease, Alzheimer's disease and other degenerative diseases, as well as cardiac failure and spinal cord damage, are all potential targets for replacement of damaged tissues by stem cell-derived cells. The Human Fertilisation and Embryology Authority (HFEA) had been of invaluable benefit in setting the conditions under which embryonic stem cell studies could be carried out, so when the opportunity arose to allow the use of such cells to study not only human fertility but also other serious human diseases, I was very supportive. This came about when a change to the original Human Fertilisation and Embryology Act to allow this to happen was proposed in 2001. In the second reading I said, after mentioning my interests and my involvement with medical research charities:

One could say that these charities have a vested interest, after all many have been set up largely to support patients and their carers and to make every effort to search for cures for their suffering. And this is not a small minority of the population about which we are talking. We have heard mention of thousands, tens of thousands, hundreds of thousands. In fact, when you add them all up, millions of people suffer from or care for patients with these diseases for which the charities have an interest.

I know that no one anywhere, let alone in your Lordships house, argues against the need for research that has the potential to help these unfortunate people. But the arguments here, as we have heard, rest not simply on the potential benefits but on the balance between those benefits and the anxieties expressed about the use of human embryos to achieve them.

Two kinds of disquiet have been exposed. The first is expressed by those who feel strongly, for religious or moral convictions, that research with human embryos, at any stage, is wrong under any circumstances. I respect their views but cannot accept that black-or-white position for reasons that I will explain in a moment or two.

The other anxiety, which many of your Lordships have expressed, is the fear that the proposals being made will open Pandora's box and lead inevitably down the slippery slope to all kinds of repugnant outcomes and, furthermore, that it is all being rushed through without adequate debate and discussion.

I believe that those fears are unfounded for several reasons. First, the idea that the natural progression of this research will lead to cloning of human beings is difficult to sustain because a licence to do so would not be granted by the HFEA. It would be a criminal act likely to lead to imprisonment and, furthermore as we have heard, the government is intent on putting this crime into primary legislation. The idea that some aberrant scientist in a basement laboratory or some multinational industry would be able to take this on secretly, outside the law, seems intrinsically unlikely. If there were people around intent on such villainy, they would not be waiting for your Lordships to decide whether to pass this legislation, they would be doing it now.

The fact that no one is doing such research now, nor would do so in the future, is because research with human embryos is so circumscribed and regulated. The number of in vitro fertilisation laboratories in the UK that are capable of this type of stem cell research is unlikely to be more than five or six. The work requires teams of doctors, scientists and technicians, as well as consenting women and men to donate eggs and sperm. It is not the kind of thing that can be done in secret. Furthermore it is not in anyone's interest to carry out such activity in secret.

The question of whether adult, instead of embryonic, stem cells could be used is clearly an important one. If stem cells derived from adults were sufficient, they would offer enormous advantages. It is an approach that is attracting a great deal of interest from scientists around the world. Others have spoken at length about the relative advantages of adult and embryonic stem cells and I shall avoid repeating those arguments. However, I should like to make the point that these are not mutually exclusive types of research; they are complementary. Embryonic stem cell research is an essential part of the wider stem cell research programme. It is clear, despite reports to the contrary, that adult stem cell research alone is a long way off from the Holy Grail.

Finally I would like to say a few words about the question of whether adequate time has been allowed for full debate of the issues. Firstly, it has been 10 years since the HFE Act was passed that allowed research on human embryos. Then, 2 years ago, the Human Genetics Advisory Committee and the HFE Authority published the results of their public consultation exercise on cloning. Over 1,000 bodies and individuals were approached directly by those groups and the questionnaire was sent out on their websites. They received a large number of responses from across a broad spectrum of people, and their measured resumé was based on a thorough analysis of the responses and on their views.

It is worth remembering that the membership of the HFE Authority included three lawyers, three broadcasters, a Bishop, a professor of theology and a psychologist. I'm not sure why the psychologist was there, probably for the members. The authority was not, and is not, loaded with scientists. It is chaired by Ruth Deech, who commands much respect.

Then last summer, the Donaldson report was published. That committee also sought views widely in formulating its report. It received over 1,000 responses to its consultation. Again I remind the house, that it had amongst its membership a lawyer, an ethicist and a reverend gentleman. The Wellcome Trust commissioned a public consultation exercise, the Nuffield Council on bioethics has produced some considered views, and finally the wide press coverage given to the Donaldson report was generally very supportive. It is difficult to know what further information or facts could emerge from yet another committee, even one as distinguished as a select committee of this House is likely to be.

Meanwhile, the patients are suffering. The 27 new cases of Parkinson's disease diagnosed every day, the diabetics, the stroke patients and those with spinal-cord injuries are simply waiting for help. They know as much as anyone that there are no quick fixes and that the results of research done today may take years to produce practical benefits for them or for those who come after them. No one is under any illusion about that. But they feel that a delay of even a year or two is intolerable. I heard a patient with cystic fibrosis say recently that what this research, with this type of future potential, gave him was hope, and hope now. I am sure that your Lordships would not wish to deny him that hope and that you agree to the amendment proposed by the noble lord, Lord Walton, which would at least allow that precious time to be saved.

I should explain that the Walton Amendment allowed a change in the law to go ahead without having to wait for yet another review of the evidence. In the event, this amendment was accepted by a large majority, 212 for and 92 against.

A select committee was set up subsequently to review the whole field, including the ethics.

I sat on that committee and learnt much from the many experts we interviewed. Among other interviewees, I listened with considerable interest to the views of the three major religious leaders. I paid particular attention to Dayan Ehrentrau, a senior rabbi and judge of the Beth Din, the Jewish court of law, fully expecting him to say that research on human embryos was forbidden. Instead, he was entirely pragmatic and, to my mind, rational, when it was explained to him that the embryos to be used in the research were those left over after in vitro fertilisation and were to be destroyed anyway. He argued from the principle that anything that can be done to help to cure disease and thereby save human life was valid given that these embryos were destined for destruction in any case. It was interesting to note that the other religious leaders were less sanguine and had reservations about experiments on these embryos. Their views were somewhat less clear cut.

Since that time there have been several more debates on embryo research as the field has developed and new possibilities have arisen. Most notable of late has been the prospect of a subset of human cloning that would allow certain diseases caused by mutations in the mitochondrial genes to be prevented. Mitochondria sit outside the cell nucleus, in the cell sap (cytoplasm) of the egg, and do not contain genes that determine any of the characteristics that influence what it is to be a human being. The latter genes are all contained within the nucleus whereas mitochondrial genes, outside the nucleus, are responsible for providing the energy that keeps cells alive and well. As the mitochondria lie outside the nucleus and in the cytoplasm of the egg cell, researchers in Newcastle have been struggling with a way of replacing the cytoplasm of an egg cell carrying the faulty mitochondria, with healthy material derived from a normal egg. This they have managed to do by taking the nucleus, containing all the normal genes, out of the faulty cytoplasm and placing it into a healthy egg cell from which its own nucleus has been removed. Nuclear replacement is then achieved and, after fertilisation with a healthy sperm in the test tube we have two sets of normal parental genes ready for transmission to the next generation, but without the faulty mitochondria causing disease in cells' energy supply processes. Experiments using empty egg cells but with intact mitochondria have been derived from both human and animal eggs experimentally and now the Newcastle workers are on the verge of being able to use this technique to prevent a series of nasty, and uniformly fatal, diseases. It has been necessary to ensure that the HFEA is able to make a careful judgement of whether this type of procedure can be undertaken and no doubt further legislation will follow.

Anonymity and sperm donation

In 2004 a new regulation was passed in which children born after sperm donation were to be allowed to know who their biological father was if they so wished. Until then they were allowed only a limited amount of non-identifiable information about their biological father and many were not even told that they had been conceived in this way. The case was made, and accepted in the Lords, that, at the age 18 years, children had a right to know not only how they were conceived but also much more about their biological parents than hitherto.

On the face of it this seemed entirely reasonable if you believed in the rights of children but it did pose a dilemma for others. In particular it could infringe the rights of another group of people, namely the sperm donor fathers who may wish to remain anonymous. There was a separate awkwardness in the regulation that children would have to wait until they were 18 to be told. The reason why delay until this particular age was chosen was never clear.

I laid out the ethical and practical difficulties that I saw with this change in the law during the debate on 9 June 2004:

> I am strongly in favour of the regulations that give children the right of access to non-identifying information about their biological parents. More than that I reiterate the point implied by the noble earl, Lord Howe, in his question about why children must wait until the age of 18 before they are allowed access to such information. I would have thought it is not unreasonable for them to have this sort of information much earlier. I also very much agree with the noble Baroness Lady Warnock, about the need for children born in this way to have information about how they were conceived.
>
> But as regards paragraph 3 of the regulations, I'm sorry to have to say that, despite the eloquence of my noble friend Lady Andrews, I am much less persuaded of the validity of the right to identify a biological parent, when that parent no longer wishes to be identified 18 years downstream. There is a balance to be struck here between one individual's right to know and another's right to anonymity. It is not all one way. In other medical matters, we betray confidences and get round anonymity with great difficulty. We put up all sorts of barriers to prevent personal data, and medical information about oneself, getting out into another domain.
>
> Let me give a couple of examples. Imagine the case of a young man, often a medical student who, perhaps because he has seen the distress of infertile

couples, decides to become a sperm donor. Perhaps under the new regulations, he agrees now to give up his anonymity to any offspring of the donation. Then 18 years later, when he is likely to be married with a couple of children conceived with his wife, he is faced with a biological child, or perhaps up to 10 of them as is allowed, whom he probably did not even know existed. Having agreed originally, he may now feel quite differently about a newfound child, as indeed may his wife, and his children born to her. Some embarrassment certainly, but much more importantly, considerable stress may be put on the marriage. Nowadays 50 per cent of marriages are shaky anyway.

Then there is the sense of responsibility suddenly acquired. Currently no legal responsibility is envisaged, but who knows what may follow in 18 years' time. In any case, a feeling of some responsibility cannot be denied and financial responsibility may follow, all of which will add to the stress on his family.

My noble friend Lord Winston has given me an example of the woman who donates her eggs to another infertile woman. Often the donor women are going through an IVF programme and their spare eggs are given altruistically to others. Many such women fail themselves to conceive with IVF and they then face the unhappy prospect of meeting a child 18 years later who is genetically half theirs but whom they had never known existed. Again that is a further stress to childless couples, already likely to feel deprived. Of course it is possible that some may be pleased with the news, but I fear that more will be distressed.

It was said that potential donors will be counselled before being asked to agree to being identified in 18 years' time and then again later, but I believe that young men will run a mile, or go ahead and live to regret it. Who of us, when we were undergraduates, could have predicted how we would feel in 18 years' time? It therefore seems likely that we will see a fall in the number of sperm donors in the immediate aftermath of the regulations. Clearly today is not the day to try to remove these regulations but I believe that we need much more evidence, more research into the full impact on all participants, not just the children and the parents raising the child. I hope that I can persuade the government, at the very least, to support more research into the impact on donors and their families of the loss of anonymity and to reconsider this whole issue in the light of that research when the 1990 Human Fertilisation and Embryology Act is revisited as I hope it will be.

Quite apart from the equal rights issue for both the child and the donor, the potential reluctance of a donor when he or she is told of the downstream consequences is likely to reduce the numbers coming forward. This, sadly, is indeed what has happened.

Jewish medical ethics

I was encouraged by Dayan Ehrentrau's evidence to the select committee on human embryo research to look at the Jewish attitude to the many ethical dilemmas facing medicine. I gave a talk on the subject, at the behest of the Maimonides Foundation, an organisation dedicated to encouraging mutual respect and interaction between Muslims and Jews, of which I was a member at the time. I became a little less ignorant after talking to the Dayan and reading a little more on the subject. I had thought that I would find a rigid reactionary position but instead I was impressed by the enlightened practicality of much of Jewish medical ethics. I reproduce that talk, for those interested in this subject, on the RCP's website: **www.rcplondon.ac.uk/forks-in-the-road**

A variety of roles

I was anxious that I might find myself at a loose end as I stood down from the RCP in 1997. I need not have feared as a number of interesting opportunities opened up for me. These included chairmanship of the Public Health Laboratory Service, a role as scientific adviser to the Association of Medical Research Charities, chairmanship of the UK Forum on Genetics and Insurance and a request to chair a panel to examine the organisation of the health services in London. I also became a trustee of a number of charities including the Wolfson Foundation. The difficulty I then had of trying to keep so many balls in the air was one that I had not predicted.

Here I outline a little of what some of these jobs entailed. They were varied in their scope but each had some fascination. They certainly taught me a lot.

Reviewing London's health services[54]

In 1997 Frank Dobson, the secretary of state for health, proposed that the health services in London should be reviewed and set up a panel to do so. He had been appointed by Tony Blair in the recently elected Labour government and was over the moon with his new senior post. He came to a meeting at the RCP and spoke of his feeling 'like a cat with nine tails' at his appointment. That meeting had been initiated by a group of 'significant' figures in the medical world who felt that it would be a good thing to be able to speak with one voice to advise the new government on health matters. The group comprised about 13 individuals representing the colleges, the BMA, the postgraduate deans, the Specialist Training Authority, deans of medical schools and the joint consultative committee – the great and the good and a marvellous idea, but one that was destined to fall out of favour, first because there was some concern among those who were excluded from this rather secretive, select group of individuals. Then there was the problem of agreeing an agenda to which they could all sign up, and the final nail in the coffin was the lack of interest in listening to our joint wisdom by the government. Little wonder then that it soon fell into disuse – another of those transient bodies.

One happy result, however, was my getting to know Frank Dobson who then asked me to chair the panel to look at London's health services.[54] This was an interesting exercise in many ways, not least in my being able to see at first hand the tensions between Frank, as secretary of state, and Alan Milburn, the minister in his department. They did not always see eye to eye on how the services in London should be improved, Alan having a much stronger desire to see radical change whereas Frank was more cautious. Perhaps Frank's constituency being in London made him more aware of the sensitivities surrounding issues such as hospital closures. This was particularly the case in relation to Bart's Hospital as I describe in a moment. Officially I was under the wing of Alan, but Frank made sure that I reported directly to him before letting Alan see any of our reports. Neither Frank nor Alan tried in any way to influence the panel in its work but I had to trip lightly between the two of them.

My panel included Sir Brian Jarman, professor of general practice and a leading light in Dr Foster's, a medical data-mining organisation; Professor Ian Cameron, provost and vice chancellor, University of Wales College of Medicine; Denise Platt, head of social services and health, the Local Government Association; and Francine Bates, assistant director, the Carers Association. We had the services of the admirable Ann Stephenson, a senior civil servant seconded from the Department of Health, who made sense of our discursive debates and set them out with admirable clarity.

Our main purpose was to examine London's health services and make recommendations about their provision.

We had a legacy from the Tomlinson report of some eight years previously, in which the main proposals included a reduction in the number of hospital beds in London with a greater reliance on hospitals outside London, a redistribution of specialised services, so that they could be focused in a smaller number of major sites, and improvements in primary care provision. There was considerable opposition to at least some of these when the report was published and in the event not all of its recommendations were put into effect by a Conservative government in which the responsible minister was Virginia Bottomley.

We learnt the lesson that if our own recommendations were to be accepted we would have to gain the trust not only of the government but also of those working in the field. We set about this by embarking on a listening exercise in which we took evidence from a wide variety of organisations and individuals.

We visited virtually all the major hospitals and many smaller ones. We spent time in a number of general practices of different sizes and met representatives of local authorities, social services and the ambulance service.

We spoke to many senior managers of the service and the chief executives of the north and south London regional health authorities. In some potentially threatened hospitals we met large groups of doctors and nursing staff as well as management and we received over 1,500 letters. Brian Jarman in particular was a goldmine of data on hospital beds, GPs and patient flows.

We discovered some remarkable facts. Some 12 per cent of the British population live in London and a high proportion of the most deprived people live there; 39 per cent of the most deprived electoral wards are in London. About 45 per cent of Britain's ethnic minority population and around 100,000 refugees lived in London, whereas almost 80,000 others were thought to be homeless. The latter were mostly single people living in hostels or sleeping rough. These facts, plus the observation that a recent survey had shown that 13.5 per cent of all housing in inner London was unfit for human habitation, were obvious measures of the increased health burden being placed on community and hospital services. Compounding factors were the high incidence of drug misuse and mental illness among homeless people, the concentration of patients with AIDS and the large influx of overseas visitors, each of which posed special difficulties for health services.

These data were critical in trying to work out whether there were too many, or too few, beds in London compared with the rest of the country. We came to the conclusion that there was no excess of beds and indeed the extra pressures on services in London suggested that any reduction would be potentially damaging, especially given the parlous state of community services.

We also found that, despite much investment in primary care, GP services lagged woefully behind those in the rest of the country. Many practices were in poor premises and the proportion of single-handed practitioners was too high. Recruitment was difficult and the total number of GPs had fallen by 1 per cent whereas the population of London had risen by 1 per cent since the Tomlinson report. We recommended a renewed recruitment drive, greater flexibility in employment and rewards, and an increase in the number of nurse specialists to work in primary care.

It is interesting that, in view of the recent proposals in the Health and Social Care Act 2012 about GP commissioning of services, we were happy then to recommend a model in which 60 or 70 GPs provided and commissioned services for 100,000 patients or more.

We felt that the strict division between the health service and social services was detrimental to the overall care of patient populations and were keen to promote greater joint, integrated working where this could be achieved. Joint budgets, although highly desirable, were very difficult to achieve within the legislation under which we were working.

Investment in community care facilities was desperately needed, especially trained carers and outreach nurses, to help support people in their homes. We needed more long-stay and intermediate care beds in the community, and argued that better use of some NHS buildings for community care could help relieve the pressure on hospital beds.

In these 1998 proposals at least, I cannot say we were very successful because the problems and possible solutions being bandied about today sound terribly familiar.

Relationships between local authorities and NHS trusts were too often strained as they each struggled with limited budgets but we urged greater effort to be put into collaboration. Recent 'urgent' discussions now, in 2014, have a very familiar ring to them.

We also examined the provision of mental health services where there were clear deficiencies that we were eager to see corrected. A mental health strategy for London as a whole was sorely needed and we proposed that joint NHS/community planning for mental health should be a priority.

Among the self-inflicted difficulties that beset the way in which London's health services were organised was the close juxtaposition of too many authorities, both health and local. With 16 health authorities, the majority of which covered two or more London boroughs, and with boundaries that had little regard for the different populations with their differing health needs, it was clear that an overarching body was needed to take a strategic view across London. Multiple boundaries, increasing in complexity the nearer the centre one came, made cross-border patient movements a nightmare of bureaucracy.

In short, London's population, which includes a high proportion of vulnerable people, was being cared for by services of a very variable standard, not helped by complex organisational structures and boundaries.

The Public Health Laboratory Service, of which I was chairman at the time, had developed an interesting scheme to unify public health surveillance for infectious diseases across London. This model had two large hospital-based laboratories as the focus for a network of collaborating laboratories around greater London. This was a valuable model for a unified, London-wide body for planning other public health functions.

One of the more straightforward problems was the division between the two regional offices of the NHS that introduced a barrier to planning services for patients moving between north and south of the river. We therefore recommended an amalgamation of the two regional offices and were pleased that this was later instituted.

To try to rationalise the multiplicity of health authorities we proposed a number of mergers to form five sectors to match the ways in which the medical schools had merged. We were gratified to see these changes accepted and put into effect. We were aware, however, that there was much more work to be done in trying to make health and local authorities a co-terminus if they were going to develop close working relationships. We felt that these were essential if patients were to be treated in a seamless way across the hospital and community divide. We recommended that joint budgets would be a significant boost to providing an integrated service but recognised how difficult this was to achieve in most places.

Inevitably most public and media attention was focused on potential hospital closures even though recommendations on primary care, mental health services and integration of health and social service budgets were at least as important and took up most of our report.

A good case had been made to go ahead with the redevelopment of University College Hospital (UCH). This hospital had existed in a number of separate buildings, including its 'cruciate' building, an iconic but inefficient structure, for very many years and had long been the subject of frustrated plans. I remember, in 1961, as a newly appointed registrar at UCH, I parked my little car with others on a piece of derelict ground known as the 'Odeon' site. An Odeon had existed there in the distant past but I was told that I would not be able to park there for long because it was to be the site of the new UCH. Now, some 36 years later, I was in a position to suggest that they should go ahead. The proud, new UCH stands out on Euston Road as a sign of a modern NHS, but it is also symbolic of a sluggish system too often causing many years of frustration and delay.

The panel was impressed with the way in which the University of London had persuaded a number of separate medical schools to come together. This made our job of suggesting rationalisation of services for optimum delivery that much easier. For example, the merger of St Mary's, Chelsea and Westminster, Charing Cross and the Royal Postgraduate Medical School / Hammersmith Hospital allowed us to recommend that the Hammersmith should continue to fulfil its important role as a leading postgraduate and research-led institution. We were able to allay much free-floating fear that the Hammersmith might be transferred to Charing Cross, as had been first muted in the Tomlinson report.

'Saving' Bart's

One of the most difficult and contentious decisions that we had to take was on the future of St Bartholomew's Hospital (Bart's) and a potential redevelopment of the Royal London Hospital. The big question was should Bart's be closed and transferred to the 'London' site. We were lobbied both for and against this by strongly partisan supporters. We were faced by large groups of sometimes hostile clinicians and other advocates making their cases.

The arguments were as follows. The Royal London, sited in a heavily populated area, was old and desperately needed redevelopment. No one disagreed with that. Bart's, on the other hand, a venerable building sitting in the City of London, had a minute catchment population that could hardly justify its continued existence where there were few who needed its acute services. The case for consideration then was closure of Bart's and transfer of its existing services into a new building at the Royal London in Whitechapel. However, the problems with this seemingly straightforward solution were many. Leaving aside the emotional attachment of the staff and many powerful advocates in the City to the historic buildings at Bart's (some structures going back to the 12th century), and ignoring the fact that Bart's was extremely wealthy with a large endowment that allowed them to make many of their own capital developments, there were a number of more legitimate reasons for the continued existence of Bart's.

First it provided a number of highly specialised services of significance for the whole of the region to the east of London and out to the coast, including oncology, cardiology and renal services. If Bart's were to close it would be vital for these services not to be lost; they would need to be transferred to the Royal London. The question then was whether a new-build could accommodate the Bart's regional specialties as well as all the existing services at Whitechapel. A quick calculation revealed that a minimum of 1,300 beds would be needed at a cost that far exceeded any new hospital building hitherto put up. We felt that such a large build was unrealistic at that time and as a result the regional specialty services would be squeezed out by the immediacy of local acute activities. It seemed important to protect these specialised services and that a better solution would be to retain them at Bart's to achieve this. The retention of the accident and emergency services was, however, clearly not justified by the minute resident population being served. The much larger daytime population coming into the city could be served by a minor injury 'drop-in' service while major emergencies during the day could be treated at the London or UCH.

Of course the retention of Bart's, even in its slimmed-down specialised form, was controversial and many at the London Hospital, including the chief executive for the joint health authority, were strongly opposed to the idea. They felt that the continuation of Bart's would not only detract from developments at Whitechapel but would also be a long-term drain on resources since running two establishments was bound to be more expensive than one.

We decided to get a financial analysis by an independent auditor of a scenario in which Bart's closed and another in which it remained open. In due course their report came to us with what looked, superficially at least, to be a clear demonstration that running Bart's and the London as two entities was vastly more expensive than running a merged operation at Whitechapel. I was rather suspicious of these conclusions and spent many a late evening going through the figures. I discovered that the auditors had loaded the two-site option with a number of services that were irrelevant to the scheme that we had outlined for Bart's. Services that were never in our thoughts as possibilities for Bart's were included in the calculations. It seemed to me that, although the original figures favoured a one-site solution, when I reworked them I came out with a different conclusion. It was true that two sites were more expensive than one but the difference between them was very small and certainly much less than the advisers had suggested. I do not know whether they had been less than independent but my sense was that the report was unreliable and could not be used to help us reach our decision.

I wrote that part of the report myself and laid out the reasons for the retention of Bart's as a hospital providing a limited number of highly specialised, regional services but that its accident and emergency service should be closed. There was a full and searching discussion in our panel and finally a form of words was agreed by all, and that was what was published in our report.

Unfortunately that was not the end to it. Although the Bart's supporters were delighted, those at the London were dismayed. I had hoped that now recommendations had been made the hospital trust would get on and start their programme of building the much-needed new hospital at Whitechapel. But instead of moving forward, the staff continued to argue about the size and content of their hospital and plans were repeatedly delayed. Some two years later I was asked by the chairman of the North London Regional Office of the NHS to return to the London and make further proposals to try to undo the snarled-up plans. The professor of surgery there, Norman Williams, was particularly concerned about how the consultant surgical team was going to be able to cover any surgical emergencies that might arise in patients at Bart's. I was not impressed by his demands for a considerable number of extra lecturers to cover such problems. I had noted that there was a large group of part-time consultant surgeons and support staff, and I felt that it should not be impossible to arrange a safe rota for surgical cover with a modest increment in staff numbers. My recommendations were not particularly welcomed but I did gain some confidence in making them from private discussions with a number of distinguished independent surgeons. I was also aware of what had been achieved in many other split-site hospitals with smaller staff numbers.

The result of this endless debate was that it took many years before the Royal London Hospital began an extensive and complicated rebuild in Whitechapel and the delay was largely self-inflicted.

I was delighted when Frank Dobson stood up in parliament and announced that all of our recommendations had been accepted by the government. He told me privately that Tony Blair had read and approved the report too. It is worth remembering that, although some of our proposals would need additional funding, this, in 1998 and with a new Labour government, was less of a problem than at other times. Labour was keen to enhance an NHS that was widely regarded as having been starved of funds by the previous government. At about 6.5 per cent of the GDP, funding for health in the UK was well down the list in the EU. So although the new chancellor of the exchequer, Gordon Brown, was urging caution and prudence and the prime minister, Tony Blair, was keen on 'modernisation'. There was an acceptance that something needed to be done for the health service in London and here was a quick political win. Our proposals were accepted and to a large extent they were put into action. Of course that was never going to be the end and, although much has changed since then, there is inevitably a gap between aspirations and achievement.

Public Health Laboratory Service: under the government's heavy thumb

One of the more enjoyable jobs I took on was the chairmanship of the board of the Public Health Laboratory Service (PHLS). This was an organisation that did a remarkably effective job of protecting the population from outbreaks of infectious diseases but this work was largely unsung. I only vaguely understood what it did when I took the job on but was rapidly made aware of the invaluable role that it played with such distinction. Its chief executive was Diana Walford, a remarkably able and effective woman, who was devoted to the organisation and ran it extremely efficiently. She had been deputy chief medical officer before this post and before that had trained as a haematologist. But it was as a manager of the PHLS that she excelled. She later became warden of Mansfield College in Oxford and ran that with great distinction too. I mention this because, in light of later developments, I want to get across how well it was run and how well it did the job that it was designed to do.

The PHLS had two major divisions, the microbiological laboratory section and the epidemiological section. The laboratories included a large central reference laboratory at Collindale in north London, and a widely distributed series of regional laboratories and smaller district/hospital level laboratories. This wide network of labs, all directed at picking up local outbreaks of infection and rapidly determining the type and nature of the organisms concerned, as well as their sensitivities to antibiotics, formed a vital part of the organisation. It was our nervous system connected to the central lab where the highly specialised testing, not available everywhere, could be done and where it was possible for an outbreak in one part of the country to be linked to outbreaks elsewhere. In this way the epidemiologists were able to track the spread of infections before they became epidemics and gain clues about what might be responsible for the spread, whether by human or animal vectors. It was in these complicated determinations that they were engaged and it was essential for the two sections of the PHLS, the microbiologists and epidemiologists, to work closely with each other.

There were expert teams working on every type of infection that one can imagine, from AIDS to tuberculosis, from influenza epidemics to food poisoning outbreaks, and from sexually transmitted infections to measles and mumps. We were instrumental in running vaccination and immunisation programmes and following them up to determine their effectiveness. For example, we warned of the danger of measles in children when MMR immunisation rates fell in the 1990s.

I have laboured the point about the valuable work that this body did because I wanted to emphasise the seriousness of the damage that was to be done to it shortly before I stood down and subsequently.

But first I should describe the problems that a chairman of an 'arm's length' body must face in being responsible to a government department. Diana and I had six-monthly meetings with whoever happened to be the minister responsible for public health. During my time in office, 1997–2004, there were at least three ministers to whom we reported: John Horam, Yvette Cooper and Tessa Jowell. Of these, only Tessa Jowell showed any real interest in the PHLS and only she managed to squeeze a little more money for our work out of the Treasury. Horam, in the Tory government, was an ex-businessman whose main interest appeared to be in our 'bottom line' rather than the work that we were doing. Yvette seemed disinterested from the word go. She was bored by public health and her eye was clearly fixed on higher things. She moved on fairly rapidly to be replaced by Tessa who was much more involved. Tessa visited the PHLS at Colindale and showed clear support for much of our work. She was convinced of the importance of what we were doing and I found her extremely helpful. On one occasion I was even the recipient of a kiss on the cheek from Tessa and it was only later, after she had climbed much higher up the slippery political slope, did I receive a peck on the cheek from Yvette. Such events live on in the memory.

But the civil servants with whom we had to deal more regularly were less than supportive. They, of course, had to keep a check on what we were doing with public money and we knew we were accountable to them. Even so, our meetings often seemed more confrontational than was necessary, and their reluctance to understand the importance of our efforts left us feeling undervalued and resentful. You might think that this is not the best way for a government to get the best out of one of its organisations. The deputy chief medical officer (CMO) in charge of our affairs was Pat Troop, a rather unsympathetic young woman who later had to learn her own lesson when she turned from gamekeeper to poacher as she was appointed as chief executive, some time after Diana stood down.

After my experience of dealing in this way with a government department, with less than fulsome support, I vowed never to take on a government post again. I did, however, break that vow later but with a rather better experience.

Despite these difficulties it was a pleasure being able to work with a group of such dedicated and effective individuals. The organisation was widely regarded internationally as being among the best and, for example, the Centers for Disease Control and Protection (CDC), our American opposite number with which we worked closely, was a great admirer. They were particularly envious of our network of laboratories around the country which provided us with much needed information about outbreaks of infection and which they lacked. It was therefore especially galling when the then CMO, Liam Donaldson, produced a report recommending a pruning of our laboratory network.

A decision had been taken on high that the work of the PHLS should be reviewed and recommendations made; it is worth recording the high-handed way in which this report was thrust upon the PHLS, which prompted my eventual resignation.

After extensive discussions in which we, and many others in the public health world, were engaged in formal and informal meetings with the CMO, there was a long period of silence. The CMO always played his cards close to his chest and there was a prolonged gap during which he considered his views. When it eventually emerged the report had some valuable recommendations and some that were frankly dangerous. On the positive side was the proposal to amalgamate the Radiation Protection Service, the Biological Standards Laboratory and the PHLS to form a new body, the Health Protection Agency (HPA).

There were cogent reasons why all these bodies, each concerned with aspects of public safety, should be brought together and the epidemiological functions of each had much in common. Joint working had clear economic advantages too.

But the severe reduction in the number of peripheral laboratories devoted to public health surveillance activities was a blow. In the event we managed to salvage some of our large regional laboratories but the public health microbiologists based in district hospitals were axed while their roles were to be taken over by the routine staff.

There had long been some envy of our laboratories by the routine NHS laboratories because our laboratory had seemed better funded, but the idea that routine laboratories would take on public health activities demonstrated an ignorance that was hard to credit. Community surveillance, monitoring of water supplies and the like, retention of the personnel trained in the specialised testing needed, liaison with local public health staff and the day-to-day interaction with the Reference Laboratory Service at Colindale were all threatened. These were just the parts of our service that the Americans had admired and envied. We protested to no avail; few understood the significance of what was being destroyed and put our protestations down to self-interest.

At this point, to paraphrase Douglas Black, 'my admiration for the Department of Health had plenty of room in which to grow'. Communication with the department became somewhat strained and as a result I felt it necessary to stand down. Phillip Hunt, then a health minister in the Lords, persuaded me to stay on a little longer while a successor was sought but the fun had gone out of the job for me and I was glad to be out of it.

It is of interest that a senior American (ex-CDC) staff member became chief executive of the HPA at a time when it, in turn, became threatened by the new Conservative administration. In 2012, when the secretary of state for health, Andrew Lansley, produced his health service reforms, he included changes to the HPA without much thought for the damaging consequences.

The Lansley bill proposed a complete shake-up of public health with the formation of a new body, Public Health England (PHE), into which the HPA was to be rolled up. This in itself would be a reasonable proposition were it not for the fact that the new body was to be managed by the Department of Health with the CMO as its chief executive and under a direct line of responsibility to the secretary of state. In short, it would lose its independent board and at the same time its ability to raise external research grant support from non-government sources. Mr Lansley would become its managing director, whether or not he had any idea about laboratory microbiology or epidemiology and, most likely, no specialist knowledge whatsoever. After much discussion, as the bill wound its way through the House of Lords, with a number of amendments, the government reluctantly agreed to a modest amelioration of their approach. The new PHE instead of being completely taken over by the Department of Health would be made an executive agency of the department, and would have an externally appointed chief executive together with an independent board. The sting in the tail, however, was that the board would only be an advisory board and the chief executive would still have direct responsibility to the secretary of state. We were thankful for small mercies and recognised that future secretaries of state, lacking the zeal for public health of the then incumbent, and recognising the futility of trying to run a highly specialised service from Westminster, would opt out of this role and devolve responsibility to the 'advisory' board. Fortunately, too, a commitment was given to allow PHE to have access to the external research grant income that would allow them to do the research necessary to stay ahead of the ever-mutating microbes threatening the public. In any event, I believe the service still suffers from its inability to pick up and follow outbreaks at its central intelligence agency because of its limited network of laboratories.

It is too soon to know whether the activities of the HPA parts of PHE will be enhanced or impaired by these changes but my guess is that the impressive staff will try their best to continue their high-quality work whatever the administrative changes thrust upon them. The efforts of governments to improve a service by altering the management structure without involving the staff who provide this service are mostly futile or, worse, damaging and costly. I fear that this is the case in this instance.

DNA, risk and the insurance industry: the UK Forum on Genetics and Insurance

Shortly after I stood down from the RCP in 1997 I was asked to chair a new body that had been set up to bring together the insurance industry and geneticists. There were increasing concerns that, with the rapidly developing ability to diagnose genetic predispositions to diseases, insurers would be keen to use their clients' genetic data to influence their premiums or even to refuse insurance to those considered to be at high risk.

The industry was concerned that the government might introduce legislation to ban the use of such genetic data and had agreed not to use this information in a voluntary, and temporary, code of practice. There was, therefore, a need to explore the long-term consequences of the increasing availability of genetic information on the insurance industry. Chris Daykin, the then government actuary, was the instigator of the committee and we met in the grand and archaic buildings of the Faculty and Institute of Actuaries in Staples Inn on Holborn.

Members of the Forum that I chaired included representatives of the insurance industry, including the chairman of Equitable Life before its demise, statisticians and geneticists.

We tried to understand how insurance companies set their premiums and stratified clients according to their presumed risk. Age, gender, family and past medical history are all taken into account and various weightings applied. What became clear was that this often seemed more of an art than an exact science. Although the actuaries tried hard to predict risk according to formulae based on data from a very large number of people, these turned out to be rather rough estimates as far as any single individual was concerned.

The geneticists, on the other hand, were concerned with the rapid growth of information about the genetic basis for specific diseases. A considerable number of monogenic diseases, that is those due to a single specific gene defect, had been discovered. Most of these cause diseases that manifest themselves in childhood and hence are of little relevance to insurers who almost entirely focus on adults. There are extremely few single-gene diseases that first become obvious in adulthood, Huntington's disease being the most obvious example. Here, possession of the predisposing gene predicts virtually completely that the possessor will develop the disease at some time, although, even there, exactly when the disease may make its presence known is not always clear.

On the other hand, an increasing number of diseases were being found to be associated with a combination of genes. These so-called susceptibility genes render an individual liable to develop a disease given exposure to certain environmental hazards, that is a given gene combination in an individual might increase their susceptibility to a disease, but do not predict with any accuracy whether that individual would actually develop the disease. There are the additional, often unknown, environmental factors that determine whether a disease develops in a genetically susceptible person. As the genetic profiles of individuals were rapidly revealing their disease susceptibilities we were arriving at a position in which everyone might be found to have a 2 or 3 per cent increased risk of developing a variety of diseases. One person might have a 4 per cent increased risk of developing diabetes, a 2 per cent greater risk of rheumatoid arthritis and a 3 per cent risk of carcinoma of the colon, whereas another might have another set of risks. As everyone has to die of something it seemed that no one is entirely risk free. These observations presented a nightmare for insurers trying to weight insurance policies according to risk.

With these two imprecise pieces of information, predicting risk by insurers using available non-genetic data and the uncertainty of geneticists to predict the degree of liability to disease based on genetic information alone, the Forum recognised that caution was needed in trying to combine two sets of such independent, and very variable, variables. It made the insurers realise that they would not be greatly hampered in their efforts to stratify risk if they were deprived of information about the genetic make-up of their clients. It certainly took any urgency out of their need to get rid of the voluntary agreement that they had reached about not seeking genetic information from their customers.

However, there remained the difficult specific issue of insurers' access to genetic tests for Huntington's disease. What if they decided, when the voluntary agreement lapsed, to use genetic tests in these afflicted individuals or their families? The disease is inherited through a dominant gene and anyone possessing the gene will almost certainly develop the disease. As it often manifests itself late in life, after sufferers have had children, half of their offspring will be statistically liable to develop the disease in later life. The question then is whether children of sufferers should be offered genetic screening. Half of them will be relieved to be shown that they are not susceptible but half will be sentenced to the certain depressing knowledge that they are liable. As insurers do take account of family history, and in these cases do not need genetic tests to determine susceptibility, they may simply load all offspring of a Huntington disease sufferer. Would these offspring feel pressurised into having tests in the hope that they may be one of the fortunate, risk-free 50 per cent when they should be insurable at normal rates?

These were difficult issues to resolve but it is fortunate that the number of cases in this position, in proportion to the total insured population, is vanishingly small. Of all insured individuals the number is likely to account for much less than 0.01 per cent. Provided that someone known to have a parent with Huntington's disease does not try to obtain extremely high-value life insurance, there was a sense that they might be insured at normal or near normal rates.

There were very instructive (to me) discussions about the overall roles of insurance. Insurance works only if the risks being insured against occur very infrequently. It follows that the majority of insured individuals do not gain anything from the scheme because they do not have a realised risk. They do, however, provide the funds that compensate those unlucky few in whom the risk is realised. Insurance is simply a system for large groups of people to share the risks by everyone contributing something to the fund. Of course, insurance companies need to make a profit for their share-holders, so that only a proportion of the money in a mutually supportive system goes out to claimants. Companies try to stratify risk so that high-risk individuals are clumped together in a group of high contributors. This is well recognised in car insurance where high-risk drivers are penalised. If, however, the stratification becomes more and more splintered, the numbers of individuals in each category become very small. At the extreme, a very small number of risk-prone individuals would have to be charged a premium close to the actual cost of the risk. Mutuality among the insured would then be threatened. Furthermore, those deemed to be of extremely low risk may feel that they do not need insurance at all. Insurance companies practising extreme degrees of stratification may find that they are no longer competitive because they will be left with only high-risk, high-premium individuals.

These sorts of consideration led the Forum to be very cautious indeed about recommending the use of even more risk factors that were being provided by the increasing number of genetic tests. The reports that we wrote during my time reflected this and many of the other points I have made here.

There were some very bright and interesting people on the Forum and it was a particular pleasure to have been given the opportunity to interact with experts from fields quite remote from my own.

The Medical Protection Society: doctors' dilemmas, misbehaviour and malpractice

In 1997 I was asked to take on the presidency of the Medical Protection Society (MPS), a mutual organisation that provides indemnity for doctors if they are accused of malpractice. It also offered cover for dentists and nurses and, by the time I became president, was the largest such organisation in the UK, covering over 120,000 practitioners worldwide.

Presidency here was a much less onerous affair than at the RCP and involved attendance at the monthly meeting of council, chaired by a much more active chairman. Despite this more restful role I became very engaged by the work of council, and was fascinated to learn about the sometimes extremely poor standards of practice of some of our medical colleagues. Having spent most of my previous life trying to raise standards, as a professor, a dean of a medical school and a president of a college, it was something of a revelation to be faced by the abysmally poor standards of some of our products.

Most of the work of the MPS took place outside council. The expert team of doubly qualified medicolegal advisers on the staff handled the innumerable telephone calls from members seeking advice. They usually dealt with these problems themselves but referred the more complicated cases to the cases committee. From there the even more tricky and potentially expensive cases, which sometimes amounted to well over a million pounds, were referred to council. It was there that I gained an idea of how carefully and thoroughly each case was examined. I also saw the true value of a mutual organisation that had some discretion, compared with an insurance-based system where little or no discretion is available. Insurance companies stick rigidly to the letter of their contracts with their clients and the small print is not always written in favour of the latter. Furthermore, insurance companies need to show a profit for their shareholders. We were often under pressure to change from a mutual to an insurance company because it was said that, as we used our discretion in some cases, we might use it against the interests of our members. We always resisted, pointing out that, in practice, we always used our discretion in favour of members and, as we were an organisation owned by our members, there was no profit motive in our activities.

It was interesting too to see how a careful balance was always struck between protecting our members' interests and those of patients who may have been harmed by our members. If it was clear that our member had been at fault we negotiated a settlement in favour of the patient and did not try to defend the case in the courts. The member was, in any case, indemnified by the MPS. If, however, the member acted against our advice and, for example, decided to contest such a case we would resist offering cover for legal and other expenses. Often a member would be accused of a misdemeanour that was groundless, or at least debatable, and we would then defend the case fully. Similarly we provided legal cover where a member had to appear before the General Medical Council. We did not, however, offer support in criminal cases.

It is always best to avoid litigation where possible and the most obvious way to accomplish this is to ensure high standards of practice. We spent much effort in education to try to achieve this. We regularly sent out information on risk avoidance with case reports illustrating specific hazards in clinical practice together with updates on good practice.

The number of complaints against doctors was rising every year as were the costs associated with some very expensive cases that could run into millions of pounds. For example, in children injured at birth the price of maintaining the care of a disabled child throughout their life was high and rising.

It was uncertain whether the increasing number and costs of cases coming to the MPS were due to a change for the worse in the behaviour of doctors or to more rapid recourse to legislation by a more critical and aware population.

Sitting in council it was easy to gain the impression that the profession at large was behaving badly. However, although there are undoubtedly a number of rogue doctors whose practice we deplored, there were others who were simply careless rather than malicious, and most of those who came to our attention were simply human and had made a rare error of judgement. The fact that repeated Mori polls show that over 90 per cent of the public trust their doctors must mean something.

I was impressed by the way in which each case reaching council was carefully and thoroughly examined both in council and by external specialty advisers. I certainly learnt a lot and often felt, when a difficult case was put under the microscope, that there but for the grace of etc, etc. I was pleased too that I was no longer in practice and that I seemed to have gone through my career with relatively few scrapes. A measure of good fortune must have been at play.

British Society of Gastroenterology

I was honoured to be elected president of the British Society of Gastroenterology for the year 2000, a good year for me, one in which I was also admitted to the Lords.

Quite a different organisation from the RCP and the presidency was very much a part-time job. Most of my predecessors had been in full-time practice but I, having retired, could devote more time to the job than others. I am not sure whether that was appreciated in the office but I did have more time to think about the Society's long-term strategy. One of my concerns was to make the Society more scientifically based. There was a perception that not enough high-quality research was being undertaken in gastroenterology, major grant-giving bodies were not supportive, and non-clinical scientists were less and less interested in contributing to the Society's meetings and other activities. Yet it was vital for the future health of the specialty for the Society to work closely with those in the more basic sciences. Transcribing the fruits of basic research into clinical practice was an important responsibility that it could not avoid. After a discussion at a 'strategic away day' a number of proposals were agreed. A new research committee would be set up with an equal number of basic and clinical scientists. It would be chaired by a basic scientist who would then become a member of council, the first basic scientist with a seat on council by right. Furthermore this new committee would have direct input to the committee concerned with making up the programme for our annual scientific meeting and responsibility for developing symposia and meetings around specific scientific themes. Much was made, too, of the need to encourage young PhD students and 'post-docs' to attend our meetings. Low entry fees and an attractive programme seemed useful ways of trying to achieve this. I was fortunately able to sell this to a society which, although always being a predominantly clinical body, could embrace the prospect of being constantly fertilised by good, relevant, basic science.

My experience at the RCP suggested to me that the Society should consider taking overseas trips to help develop international relations. I cannot now remember why Egypt was chosen as our first travel experiment, but it did excite considerable interest.

An intrepid band set off with high hopes in 2000 and we were graciously greeted by our hosts. It was something of a surprise to some of our members to find themselves doing long lists of endoscopies for the Egyptian population, but by and large we were treated well. We were taken on an unforgettable trip down the Nile. Even the confusion in the travel arrangements and not knowing whether we were ever going to get back in time to catch our plane home did not detract from the pleasure.

However, the somewhat disjointed arrangements that we encountered did not leave the Society desperate to make many more such trips after my year in office and I think that it has remained a unique occasion.

I did think that one year in office as president was a little short if he or she wanted to make any changes. After my experiment in overseas visits, however, the Society seemed a little relieved. They did agree some years later to try to overlap the roles of successive presidents to introduce some continuity into their affairs. Now the Society seems much more business-like in the way that it performs and thrives without any of my so-called innovations.

Charity world

I was approached by a number of charities after I stood down from the RCP and accepted offers to help several of them.

I became a trustee then, and later, of the Wolfson Foundation, the Foulkes Foundation, Hadassah UK, British Technion, Weizmann UK, Ovarian Cancer Action and DIPEX; at about the same time, I became scientific adviser to the Association of Medical Research Charities (AMRC). In retrospect it was, of course, too many to be taking on but each seemed such a good cause that I could not resist. Later, I became more realistic and started turning down similar approaches, but not without a sense of guilt. I found that agreeing to become a patron of a charity meant less responsibility and little work, and I tended to take this route to salve my conscience.

The Wolfson Foundation is a very wealthy charity and works extremely effectively and efficiently in distributing over £30 million a year in grants to good causes. One of the greatest pleasures in life I have discovered is giving away large amounts of money, especially if it is not your own. The Wolfson and the Foulkes Foundations were fortunate in having their own endowments so they did not have to go out to raise money. Others were constantly trying to raise funds from the public and here I was of less use to them. Not being endowed with fundraising skills I concentrated on those aspects of the charities that needed a medical or research voice. This helped get round the problem of conflicts of interest for me between the several charities of which I was a trustee.

The AMRC has over 100 member charities, including the huge Wellcome Trust, Cancer Research UK and the British Heart Foundation, as well as a long tail of much smaller charities. Collectively the AMRC give out well over £1 billion per annum for medical research, hence its considerable clout. I became its scientific adviser in 1997 at the behest of Diana Garnham, then its chief executive, and have remained in the position since then. I have seen three chief executives and four chairmen come and go, and I suppose I must be doing something right to be kept on. Either that or no one is quite sure why I'm still there and do not want to disturb the status quo. I am happy to be engaged with its activities, however, because I believe that it has done excellent work in representing member charities in discussions with government and in encouraging and supporting charities in their own activities. I suspect that I may be helpful in at least one way by speaking up for research charities in the Lords.

National Centre for the 3Rs: making research with animals acceptable

David Sainsbury was the minister in the Department for Innovation, Skills and Industry in the Labour government. He had special responsibility for research and among his many concerns was the often-strident criticism of researchers who engaged in animal experimentation. Apart from the animal welfare movements with their reasoned concerns and the less benign animal rights movements, there were the legitimate anxieties among the general public that animals should not be allowed to suffer in the name of science. Against this background there was a desperate need to pursue research using animals to gain a better understanding of diseases and in the search for new treatments. There was also the legal requirement of the regulatory bodies that drugs should be tested in animals before use in humans to ensure their safety.

Sainsbury decided that something needed to be done to reassure the public that, when animal experiments were essential, they be performed in the most humane way and, when animal use was not essential, it was stopped. The 3Rs had been expounded as the best ways in which animal experimentation might be undertaken, that is the replacement, reduction and refinement of animal research. Where such experiments could be done without animals these methods should be used instead: replacement; where that was not possible the number of animals used should be kept to the absolute minimum: reduction; and where that was not feasible those experiments that were necessary should be performed with the minimum of discomfort to the animals: refinement.

Lord Sainsbury was keen to show that the government took this matter seriously and decided to set up a National Centre for the 3Rs (the NC3Rs), and turned to me to take on its chairmanship. Although I had vowed never to take on another role working for government I found that I could not sidestep this one. I had a lot of respect for Sainsbury and thought that here was a minister with whom I could work. It was a fortunate choice because, from the beginning, we had strong government support.

Vicky Robinson was our first chief executive and that too was fortunate because she was, and is, extremely able and knowledgeable about the field and we were off to a good start.

Our big advantage was the fact that we were not antagonistic to researchers or animal experimentation and only sought best practice and the 3Rs. We engaged with both academic researchers and industry, on the one hand, and animal welfare people, on the other, and our board reflected this wide background. Surprisingly we found that there was a commonality of purpose among us. Our main focus was on funding new research into better ways of doing research with animals and sought bids from those engaged in this activity.

We awarded a prize, published guidelines on the 3Rs, held meetings for animal technicians, and entered into dialogue with the pharmaceutical industry and the academic community. And we began a large response-mode research programme. Over the years, as the organisation grew, we gained the confidence of researchers and the pharmaceutical industry and, instead of resisting what we were trying to do, they engaged enthusiastically with us.

Our funding came through the Medical Research Council and later we were able to persuade both the Biotechnology and Biological Research Council and the Association of British Pharmaceutical Industries to offer their support so that, by the end of my three-year term we had doubled our income to some £3m per annum and were able to fund increasing numbers of research projects.

One of our major successes was to demonstrate how testing drugs for safety and toxicity in animals, especially rats, was a poor predictor of toxicity in humans. The regulatory authorities that were demanding such testing began to recognise this defect and as a result industry was able to cut out some of this activity, which was costly, often unpleasant and consumed large numbers of animals. We were also able to demonstrate that different drug firms used quite variable numbers and types of animal testing, and in so doing questioned why it was necessary for some to use so many more animals than others and why such a range of species was required. This simple demonstration caused several to change their practice.

One of the most contentious areas was the use of primates in research and we tackled this head on. Gaining the confidence of the relatively small group of workers involved in this type of research to examine their practice was not an easy task but, in a series of meetings, we hammered out an agreement on better ways of doing this work involving less stress for the animals.

I was pleased to have been able to contribute to this work and by the end of my term in office I had learnt a lot. I was fairly ignorant of much of the field when I went in but it was an excellent opportunity for me to chair a group of bright, dedicated individuals and to have a high-quality, hard-working team of people behind me.

After being so closely involved with two national bodies, NC3Rs and the PHLS, I recognised how fortunate the UK is to have such devoted, able and hard-working teams of people engaged in a common purpose for the good of the population.

Chapter 12 **Israel and the Middle East**

I have taken a particular interest in Middle East affairs and spoken on many occasions in the House on these matters. My bias has always been towards Israel for a number of obvious reasons. Being Jewish predisposes me in that direction, and having a daughter and grandchildren living there makes it inevitable that I should speak up for that country in debates. I am not, however, an uncritical observer of Israel's actions and I hope that I give a fairly balanced view of the unstable situation in the Middle East. I do find myself, however, forced into a defensive position when I hear factually incorrect and misleading statements about Israel and its actions that emerge from some quarters in the Lords. There are many criticisms levelled at Israel, only some of which seem to hold water. Some of them are expressed as strongly, if not more so, in the Israeli media which do not pull their punches.

It is the case that Israel is surrounded by countries in varying degrees of turmoil and suffering.

In Egypt there is extreme poverty and 50 per cent unemployment, especially among young people. These are just the conditions under which extremism can flourish and a search for scapegoats is likely. President Morsi was depicted as a 'moderate' Islamist but he had an uphill struggle to maintain the peace treaty with Israel. His more recent removal from office and imprisonment by the army has emphasised the deep split between the Muslim Brotherhood and more secular elements in society. It remains very unclear where the country is heading but the continuing strife can hardly help the great majority of poor and unemployed people seeking a better life.

In Syria the civil war, consuming the country in such a devastating way, is revealing the increasing presence of extremists in opposition forces. Israel is unlikely to be comforted by a change from a belligerent Assad regime, hosting the Hamas leadership and arming Hezbollah in Lebanon, to one in which Sunni fundamentalists are in power.

Libya has descended into tribalism and chaos and Bin Laden's right-hand man has slipped in as deputy prime minister while, in Saudi Arabia, a currently stable bastion of Sunni Islam and an ally of the West, it is impossible to build a church, Jews cannot visit and women's rights are curtailed under Sharia law.

Iraq is in an uncertain transition with outbursts of sectarian violence and Iran is one of the two most dangerously belligerent states in the world with its combination of nuclear ambitions, extreme Shia fundamentalism and threats to the West, especially to Israel (the other is North Korea).

It is not too difficult to understand why Israelis feel under siege and why the Israel/Palestine problems seem to be only one part of their concerns. Important though they are, it is not felt that their resolution will change anything in the internal behaviour of their other unstable neighbours nor in their antipathetic attitudes to Israel.

Criticisms of Israel, valid and invalid

When Israel is slighted, to my mind wrongly, I defend her in terms that may seem biased. I do so only on those occasions in order to try to restore the balance. For example, I find the criticism that Israel is an apartheid state particularly difficult given the history of persecution of the Jews. The evidence against that slur is easy to martial. In Israel every citizen has a vote; there are currently 10 Arab members of the Knesset, seven Druze members, three of Israel's ambassadors are Arabs, and one of the supreme court judges is a Christian Arab; Arabic is one of the two official languages and included in all major road signs; Emile Habibi, an Arab, recently won the Israel prize for literature; on TV Arabs play Jews and Jews play Arabs and, in hospitals, Arab doctors and nurses treat Jewish patients, and vice versa, without any sense of discrimination. Hardly an apartheid state then.

It is unfortunately the case, however, that Muslim Arabs fare much worse in Israel than Christian Arabs. Although Christians make up only 10 per cent of the 1.5 million Arab citizens, that is about 2 per cent of the total Israeli population, they punch way above their weight. They account for about 25 per cent of the students at the Technion in Haifa and occupy a number of the academic positions. I recently had the pleasure of hearing a presentation by a young Arab medical researcher there. He had been awarded a Foulkes' prize for a high-quality piece of research by an Israeli scientist as judged by the Foulkes Foundation, of which I am a trustee. He was supervised by his orthodox Jewish professor and the respect they held for each other was obvious.

The infant mortality rates among Christian Arabs are the lowest of any country in the Middle East and, in girls, better than Israeli Jews. More Christian Arab women go into higher education than any other group in Israel. It is interesting, too, that Israel is one of only two Middle East countries where the Christian population is rising: fourfold in the last 50 years. The other is Jordan.

However, there remain problems for even this group and employment in a competitive market is difficult. Their competitiveness is reduced because of a lack of the edge that Jewish Israelis get by having served in the armed forces and formed deep bonds that continue into civilian life.

The Muslim Arab population faces even more difficulties. They are often poor, have high unemployment rates and feel marginalised. They have this in common with the Ethiopian Jews who came in during the last 20 or so years and whose integration has proved problematic. Inequalities clearly exist and discrimination occurs but that does not deny the fact that every Israeli citizen is equal under the law and has the same rights as everyone else. The Israeli organisation, Kav Mashve, with the support of the government, has been making strenuous efforts to improve the employment of Arabs in Israel. They have a long way to go.

Much more problematic is the relationship between Israel and the Palestinians in the West Bank and Gaza, and here it is difficult to get away from history and the resentment that it has engendered.

Daniel Taub, Israel's ambassador to the UK, spoke about his experiences in negotiations with the Palestinians and said that there were always three negotiations going on at the same time: one across the table, another along the table, with representatives from other government departments on your own side, and third behind the table, with your own population whom you have to satisfy. He went on to say that there is another dimension – that of time, when you are negotiating for your grandparents and their past experiences, and for your grandchildren, for the future. Too often, he said, negotiations become bogged down with the grandparents instead of for the future of one's grandchildren.

It is, however, extremely difficult to avoid looking at past history. The Palestinians mostly see Israel as an unwelcome intrusion into their lands and would like to see it removed, whereas the Israelis see Israel as their biblical homeland and a safe haven from centuries of persecution.

This is a very difficult starting point. And for Israel it is hard to avoid remembering that between 1948 and 1967 Jordan ran the whole of the West Bank. It was all Jordan then and they treated the Palestinians as second-class citizens with no hint that they might give them a homeland of their own. They also ruled the old city of Jerusalem to which no Jew was allowed anywhere near. Synagogues were destroyed, the Jewish quarter ruined and the western wall of the Temple, Judaism's holiest site, was lost to them.

They also remember that the complete withdrawal from Gaza of over 10,000 settlers in more recent years was not followed by a sense that this did the

Palestinians or Israelis any good. Thousands of rockets fell on Israel as a result and Israeli towns near the border had to sleep in underground shelters under a daily barrage of rockets.

Hamas, once it had won the election, purged itself of Fatah by killing some and driving others out.

Similarly, withdrawal from southern Lebanon left a space for Hezbollah to move into, not only much to the regret of Israel, now threatened by a battery of missiles that can reach anywhere in Israel, but also to the dismay of the Lebanese whose Christian population has left in droves.

These experiences make Israel keen to make sure that any peace deal with Fatah on the West Bank includes enough security arrangements so that they are not faced with a similar vacuum for terrorist regimes to fill. Israel is only 15 miles' wide at its narrowest point and the thought of yet more missile sites on its eastern border within a mile or so of the prime minister's office and parliament, and close to its international airport, is one that is difficult to contemplate. It could not allow another border to be dominated by the likes of Hezbollah in the north and Hamas to its west. Israel has shown willingness to exchange 'land for peace' – in Sinai and Gaza – but it has not been rewarded with much peace. The desire for peace is undoubted, but peace without security is suicidal for Israel.

On the Palestinian side resentment runs very deep. They are constantly reminded of what they were made to give up in 1948. They remember with deep hatred how they were driven out from the current Israel and they yearn to return to what they see as their rightful homeland. Despite the passage of 65 years these memories are kept fresh by constant repetition in their media and school textbooks.

This, together with the settlements in the West Bank that are ever-present reminders of occupation, keep resentment at a high level. And the behaviour of some Israeli soldiers towards the Palestinians is sometimes reprehensibly aggressive, compounding the resentment.

Another issue is the status of Jerusalem. Even there, however, the outline of a negotiated settlement seems feasible. Although stories of the takeover and 'judification' of Jerusalem are frequently relayed, it is a fact that its Arab population is rising faster than that of the Jewish population. Surprising but true. The Arab population rose from 26 per cent in 1997 to 35 per cent in 2011. Arab numbers rose by 3.2 per cent in 2011 against a rise of 2.1 per cent for the Jews. Splitting Jerusalem into an Arab and Jewish half has been on the table at various times in different negotiations. It has never gone beyond that but the fact that it has been discussed at all is significant.

The security wall built between Israel and the West Bank has had its critics since it was built. On the positive side it has undoubtedly cut the number of terrorist attacks in Israel and saved lives. On the negative side it has caused hardships for many Palestinian farmers who have seen their land bisected and separation from their olive trees. It is sometimes suggested that it has been built beyond the Green Line and on Palestinian territory. Although this may be true in some places, it is not true for the over 90 per cent which is on the Green Line, and most of it is an electrified fence rather than a wall. It seems likely that, given a future with greater security, the need for a barrier will become redundant. Unfortunately I cannot see that happening any time soon.

It is of interest that this is not the first wall to be erected to keep out potential enemies around the world, nor even the first in the Middle East. In 1938 the British built a wall, 'Taggart's wall', along a 50-mile stretch of border between Palestine and Lebanon and Syria in an effort to keep out the murderous incursions of gangs from Syria.

Israel is not sanguine either about the possible coming together of Hamas and Fatah. Hamas frequently speaks quite openly of the destruction of Israel and refuses even to contemplate the possibility of peace talks. Indeed one of the sticking points in a Hamas/Fatah agreement is Fatah's potential willingness to negotiate with Israel. A rapprochement between them would clearly make a peace deal with Israel less, rather than more, likely. It is sometimes said that Israel should talk to Hamas – 'talk to your enemies' – but the fact is that Hamas is absolutely committed to not talking to an Israel that it is unwilling to admit should exist.

There have been intermittent talks with Fatah and hopes have often been raised, only to be dashed by this or that. Usually the Palestinian Authority has insisted on the stopping of settlement building as a precondition of talks. Israel, on the other hand, points to the fact that it did cease such building for 10 months, a year or so ago, in an effort to restart the talks but the Palestinians failed to come to the table. Offers of talks without preconditions from Israel did not result in a response until the very recent pressure from the USA.

It is often said that all that stands between peace for Israel and the Palestinians is the vexed question of the settlements in the West Bank. Sort them out and all would fall into place. Although they are undoubtedly problematic, it would be naïve to think that they are the only or even the main reason standing in the way of a peace treaty.

They are often referred to as 'illegal settlements' under international law but the basis for the claim of illegality is not clear cut and there have been legal arguments that belie that claim. Nevertheless there is a strong moral and practical case for their removal from a future Palestinian state on the West Bank. Indeed their removal has been part of a number of proposals outlined in earlier negotiations including, for example, at Camp David and more recently in discussions between

Ehud Olmert, then Israel's prime minister, and Abu Mazan, the Palestinian leader. These earlier offers did not, however, include all settlements because Israel wanted to retain a number of townships close to Jerusalem with a 'land swap' of equivalent areas of land currently within Israel's Green Line. This was said to comprise about 3 or 4 per cent of the land currently occupied by settlements.

The fact is, however, that it is not simply a matter of agreeing on withdrawal from settlements. That is within the grasp of both parties even though, for Israel, it would involve the non-trivial task of rehousing up to 300,000 settlers within Israel. That this would not be a straightforward matter was starkly demonstrated by the continuing difficulties in repatriating the 10,000 settlers who were withdrawn from Gaza some years ago, together with the undoubted resistance of the extreme element within the settler movement itself. Nevertheless it is achievable if it was the only problem.

I would not wish to belittle the settlement issue. It is indeed a major stumbling block and I am firmly of the view that they should be dismantled. But to many in Israel it is not the most significant impediment to peace.

There is now a sense in Israel that Abu Mazan is not interested in peace. Evidence that he simply uses the settlement issue as the key in his public statements for the West, is to be found in his rather different messages to his own people. At home he promises a return of Palestinians to the whole of Israel through his public media pronouncements and school textbooks. In the books, Israel and the Jews are portrayed in the vilest terms possible with repeated exhortation to violence and Jihad. His rejection of the idea that Israel should be recognised as a Jewish state belies his acceptance of a two-state solution. His two-state proposal is seen by Israelis as one in which he wants both states to be Muslim Arab. A close examination of the Palestinian media, or of Abu Mazan's pronouncements, reveals no sign that he is preparing his people for two states in which one is Jewish and to which only a limited return of current Palestinians will be possible. His position has hardened since he gained limited recognition as a state at the United Nations General Assembly late in 2012.

He is also, not unnaturally, more interested in what is happening in the wider Middle East than in peace talks. The emergence of more radical regimes in the aftermath of the 'Arab spring' is potentially threatening to those wishing to seem more liberal. He, and King Abdullah of Jordan, are looking over their shoulders and are concerned for their own safety. Even if he was inclined to make a move towards a peace deal with Israel, he may well feel that now is not the best time to do so. Making peace with the arch enemy of the rest of the Arab world will not win Abu Mazan many friends, and while there remains much turmoil among his Arab neighbours he may well feel that procrastination is his best option.

We thus have a rather pessimistic picture, on the one hand of an Israel that is extremely concerned about its security and wants this to be a sticking point in any negotiations, and, on the other, of Palestinians stuck between a desire to develop a stable state of their own and an unwillingness to recognise that Israel is a Jewish state, bolstered by a fear of reprisal from Hamas and their more extreme neighbours if they travel far down the route of reconciliation.

It is the 'right of return' that has always been the sticking point. As I have intimated above, the Jewishness of the state of Israel is its whole raison d'être, and to deny that is to deny its existence. For Jews it has to remain the one country in the world that will take them in from wherever they may be persecuted. Yet the Palestinian firm position is that Palestinians, whether or not born in the current Israel, should have the right to return there, that is a state in which the huge majority would not be Jewish would be the end result. Offers of a very limited return coupled with some compensation for others is anathema to the Palestinians. Their media and textbooks testify to this view.

It is these two issues, a right of return for the Palestinians and security for Israel, that are the real reasons for a failure to reach a peaceful, two-state, solution and less so the 'settlements' where most, rather simplistic, criticism often resides.

It is against this background that the American-inspired peace initiative in mid-2013 has to be seen and, although the two parties have restarted face-to-face discussions, it is hard to find any room for optimism for the immediate future. We may have to wait on what happens elsewhere in the aftermath of the 'Arab spring' and, crucially, on how Iranian nuclear aspirations, and Israel's response to it, pan out. An Iran armed with nuclear weapons will alter the whole Middle East landscape and its dominance will make it even more difficult for a Palestinian leader to discuss peace with Israel. Quite apart from the direct existential threat to Israel, repeatedly and publicly stated by the Iranian leadership, there is the indirect threat that they pose through their proxies in Hezbollah and Hamas. However, Hezbollah has been heavily distracted and engaged in supporting the Assad regime in Syria and is losing support in its natural base in Lebanon. Meanwhile, Hamas in Gaza is also becoming more isolated as its Syrian support has been lost, and it has found that relations with the new Egyptian regime have markedly weakened.

Any Palestinian leader making a move towards peace with Israel, until Iran's nuclear capability is resolved, would be foolish if not suicidal. If Iran ceases its nuclear ambitions then the rest of the Arab world would heave almost as big a sigh of relief as Israel. That would change the possibilities for a peaceful agreement. The very recent negotiations between Iran and the USA, EU and Russia on the possibility of halting the Iranian nuclear programme in exchange for a modest reduction in the restrictions and embargoes placed on the regime has been greeted as an important step in the West. However, there has been much less enthusiasm in Israel, Saudi Arabia and the Gulf states who see it as a very poor bargain from their point of view. They see it as if Iran is being let off the hook while it continues to retain the capacity to develop a bomb in a relatively short time. Trust of the regime does not run high, least of all in Israel and Saudi Arabia.

Although this development came as a considerable, yet mostly welcome, surprise there are signs, even now, as I write at the beginning of 2014, that the Iranians are reneging on this limited first step. In such a fluid situation it is hard to place too much faith in this, nevertheless remarkable, development. All alternatives are extremely gloomy.

If the negotiations come to nought and if, as seems likely, Israel takes Iranian threats at face value and sees its future existence threatened and attacks Iran, then the future of the whole Middle East will become even more dangerous and unpredictable than it is now. Israel will be attacked from all sides, especially from Hezbollah in the north, Hamas to the west and potentially from Egypt in the south. Iran would of course retaliate and Assad in Syria may find the conflict a useful distraction from his domestic problems. The USA and the West would be inevitably drawn in by a raging Muslim anti-Western surge, and the stability of the world would be threatened. Not a future to be contemplated with any equanimity and one to be avoided at all costs. Hence the desperate need to ensure that sanctions continue to be sufficiently robust to stop Iranian nuclear ambitions. There is little room, or time, for a reduction in sanctions.

The recent successes of the 'iron dome' missile defence system that operated in the conflict with Hamas in December 2012 may have shifted perceptions in Israel about their vulnerability, but this alone will not alter the fundamental positions adopted by Iran or Israel. Nor is it at all obvious that Iran will back down, even given the most stringent sanctions, especially if support continues from Russia and China.

Gaza

In recent times we have seen a number of well-publicised attempts to break the 'siege' of Gaza, one of which ended in tragedy and another in a tense stand-off. The early attempts, occurring at a time when Israel clamped down on imports to Gaza, ignored the fact that there was another border, with Egypt, that might have been available if the Egyptians had not also been concerned about the activities of Hamas. Although Hamas and Israel see themselves at war, in more recent times Israel has allowed more goods through apart from those felt to be usable for the conflict.

It is undoubtedly the case that life for Gazan citizens is hard and at times intolerable. There are considerable restrictions on their movement in and out of Gaza, unemployment is very high and there is a shortage of medical supplies. Clean water and contamination with sewage are particular problems with water-borne diseases being far too common.

Although comparison with other humanitarian crises may be exaggerated, for example with parts of Africa where starvation and a complete lack of water and medicines prevail, the unsurprising fact is that the Gazan population is frustrated and seething with a sense of injustice.

It is, however, in the apportionment of blame for this parlous situation that questions may be raised. For example, medical supplies for Gaza are provided by Israel to the Palestinian Ministry of Health in Ramallah and they in turn transfer them to Gaza. It is in this transfer by the Palestinian Authority where delays are created. The director of the emergency room at Al-Nasser Hospital in Gaza City, Dr Nabil Bargouni, confirms as much and Tony Lawrence, head of the World Health Organization in Jerusalem, says that: 'The shortages are due to the conflict between the two (Palestinian) health ministries'.

Again the water and sewage problems are undoubtedly severe and the cause of much disease, especially in children and, although Israel's seeming indifference cannot be condoned, the difficulties cannot be placed entirely at Israel's door. Large amounts of aid do enter Gaza from the UN and other relief agencies. The United Nations Children's Fund (UNICEF) recently offered to build a much needed water desalination plant there but, when they proposed to purchase equipment from across the border in Israel, where there is considerable expertise, all hell broke loose. The Palestinian Contractors Union condemned UNICEF and announced a boycott of the agency. Other groups threatened protests against UNICEF and shut down its offices. Such is the hatred of Israel that they prefer fostering their antipathy rather than meeting the need to supply their citizens with clean water.

This is simply an example of how far Hamas will go to destroy any possible links with Israel, even to the extent of preventing or diverting the passage of goods from Israel that their population desperately needs. Despite that extreme antipathy, most supplies do get through, almost 5,000 truckloads and over 4,000 Gazans pass across the border each month. The real GDP grew, from an admittedly low base, by 25 per cent in the first three quarters of 2011. Unemployment is high at 25 per cent but this is down from the 40 per cent of two years ago (and considerably lower than the 50 per cent in Egypt). It is also remarkable that there are said to be over 600 millionaires in Gaza, created largely by Hamas from illegal trade of smuggled goods through the tunnels. They seem adept at taxing imports for personal gain. These operators are finding life harder since Egypt has been closing off the smuggling route through the tunnels. It has been said by the former Palestinian Authority's security commander in Gaza, Mohammed Dahlan, that: 'Hamas is the only party that is laying siege to Gaza; it is Hamas and not Israel or Egypt that is punishing its people'.

What is surprising is the number of patients and doctors from Gaza who are to be found in Israeli hospitals. At the Hadassah Hospital in Israel a small group of doctors and nurses from Gaza have been trained to treat children with cystic fibrosis, with the intention for them to set up a clinic on their return to Gaza where there were no paediatricians with these specialist skills. This Hadassah experience is not an isolated example. There are several paediatricians from Gaza training at children's hospitals across Israel, although this clearly can only go so far to meeting the need for specialist doctors in Gaza.

Meanwhile patients from Gaza flood into Israeli hospitals, often with advanced disease requiring extensive and expensive treatments, sometimes too late. When I visit these hospitals I have found it impossible to remain unaware of the large number of Palestinian patients in many of them. Whole Palestinian families sit with their children and they often come for months at a time, some being housed in nearby hotels. Children from Gaza make up 40 per cent of patients having cardiac surgery and chemotherapy at the Safra and Schneider Children's Hospitals and no less than 60 per cent having chemotherapy at the Dana Children's Hospital in Tel Aviv. In Ashkelon, a city close to Gaza, the hospital treats all patients regardless of origin. During the many years when rockets have been fired into southern Israel from Gaza, patients are often evacuated into underground facilities at the hospital. Paradoxically, many of these patients are from Gaza.

Senior officials in Hamas and the Palestinian Authority come to Israel for treatment. Consultations by telephone between doctors in Gaza and Israel are surprisingly common and relations at the personal level are often more than cordial.

It seems that medicine can circumvent politics in remarkable ways, although of course many of these interactions go largely unreported in the media. The fact is, however, that not only does medicine in Israel share international concerns about the humanitarian problems in Gaza, but is also actively doing something positive. Despite the extreme rhetoric emanating from Hamas, it is not this that prevents the transfer of patients into Israel. Nor is it Israeli checkpoint procedures although bureaucracy on both sides does cause delay. Much more responsible for the late referral of patients is the lack of specialist care and diagnostic facilities within Gaza. As always a lack of funds is the dominant factor. Aid is certainly required but attempting to reach those in need through, for example, high-profile 'blockade busters' serve only PR aims and have no immediate practical value. Although many point to the terrible antagonism between Hamas and Israel that threatens to derail any peace talks and will point to the blockade and the limits set by Israel on what may or may not be transferred into Gaza, this seemingly insurmountable political background can be circumvented by those on the ground in medicine.

I have spoken on all of these topics in the Lords on the many, somewhat disproportionate number of, times that they come up. There is a small number of peers who are strongly opposed to Israel and who speak with some venom against it as often as possible. On the other side there is a similar number, including myself, who speak for Israel. In the middle, where the vast, usually silent, majority sit, there are mixed views although the tendency is towards criticism, albeit less overt, of Israel. Their views are influenced by the media and sometimes seem less than fully informed.

It is difficult to gauge the opinions of the public at large but I sense that there is more Islamophobia around than anti-Israel feeling. This, however, is not the sense that one gains from much of the media. Despite its protestations of 'balance' the BBC often seems to me at least to be biased in its treatment of the Israeli–Palestinian conflict. It, and some newspapers, are rarely willing to report Israel in a positive light and reflect a view now predominant in left wing circles that Israel is the strong aggressor against an enfeebled downtrodden Palestinian population who can do no wrong. In this light, terrorists are depicted simply as militants and rocket attacks are seen as a completely understandable response to oppression. The willingness of some on the left to suggest that they are 'all Hamas now' indicates how far some have become deluded about an organisation founded on terrorism.

Efforts to boycott Israel have been hitting the news in recent years and have been driven largely by a number of trade unions. The University Lecturers Union led a campaign to boycott Israeli universities and academics. It was led by a small minority of vocal members who were not among the most distinguished of academics. Indeed leading figures, including the vice chancellors, heads of departments and professors would have nothing to do with it. The result was that this boycott had no detectable impact on academic interchange between the UK and Israel. It did, however, cause consternation among Israeli academics and it took some effort on my, and others', part to point out that it had no practical effect on academic relationships. Similar efforts to boycott Israeli goods by trade unions and other agitators have little practical impact apart from the unpleasant noise. Import of Israeli goods is rising each year and trade relations remain on a strong footing. Those pressing the boycott case have to contend with the problem that so much of our everyday technology is dependent on Israeli input, from computer software, anti-virus programmes, smart phone chips, television innovations, to say nothing of sophisticated security systems and medical technology.

I may be accused of trying to make light of these efforts to ostracise Israel and there is undoubtedly a rise in anti-Israel rhetoric, and not only in the UK. It is nevertheless important to try to retain a sense of balance. Although there is some anti-Semitism around I am not one of those who see every criticism of Israel as a proxy for anti-Semitism. Indeed, despite the pro-Israel tone of most of my remarks here, I am very critical of much of the Israeli government's policies, including those on the settlements. Nevertheless Israel has been very poor at getting its message across and has left the Palestinians to project their own sense of oppression very successfully. Only belatedly has Israel recognised its arrogance in ignoring the views of Europe and the UK that it has always regarded as being strongly Arabic, at least in the establishment. There is an element of truth in that. However, it leaves Israel open to the dangerous view in the West that 'it had it coming' if the rest of the Arab world, and Iran in particular, where anti-Israel and anti-Semitic views are uniformly profound, attack and damage or destroy Israel. Apart from in America, Israel has not won many hearts and minds, and it may come to regret its neglect of European opinion.

Although anti-Semitism seems to be relatively low key in the UK, this is not the case in much of the rest of Europe. In Poland, Norway, Sweden, some of the Balkan states, Hungary and Austria, it is becoming extremely widespread and, in some places, vehement. French Jews are buying homes in Israel in large numbers in order to have a bolthole in case anti-Semitism becomes more intolerable at home. It is prevalent in a number of South American states as well as in Malaysia and some of the Far East. And in Pakistan and the rest of the Muslim world anti-Semitic rhetoric has reached an intolerable degree, with the media, television plays and textbooks portraying Jews as the scum of the earth who should be exterminated. The *Protocols of Zion* and other extreme anti-Semitic texts are widespread in the Middle East and all of this makes Jews around the world even more concerned for Israel's future as one of the few places in the world where they may be safe.

It is no comfort to know that religious persecution in the Middle East is not confined to Jews. Christian minority communities are under considerable threat as Muslim extremists begin to prevail. I spoke about this particular problem in the Lords on 9 December 2011 and said:

Scarcely a week goes by when we do not hear of yet another outrageous attack on one or other Christian community in the Middle East. In Egypt we hear about the persecution of the Copts, in Lebanon the Christians are leaving in droves, in northern Iraq they are terrorised and in the Horn of Africa tales of persecution and worse are so commonplace that the media have more or less stopped reporting them. Even in Palestine, the number of Christian Arabs is falling rapidly. In Bethlehem, the epicentre of Christianity, they feel increasingly unwelcome and now they are marginalised where once they were in the majority. There are now barely 50,000 Christians in the whole of the West Bank. Of course, Christians are not alone in being chased out. The Baha'i faith has been eliminated from Iran and other Middle East countries, and the Jews have a long history of persecution in the region. No fewer than 800,000 Jews have been driven out in the past 50 or so years. Were it not for the existence of Israel they would be refugees and dispersed around the world. It is also the unfortunate case that I, as a Jew, would be very unwelcome in many of these countries. For example, I would find it very hard to visit Saudi Arabia; I would not be given permission to go there.

This is troubling at a time when we in the UK and the largely Christian Western societies are quite rightly leaning over backwards to accommodate people of every race, creed and religion. You have only to look around your Lordship's House to see our tolerance to diversity. At the same time, fundamentalism is increasing in the Middle East along with a dangerous anti-Christian intolerance.

There are two exceptions, possibly more, to this general pattern: Jordan and Israel. It might be instructive to examine why that might be so. In Jordan the relatively benign rule of King Abdullah has allowed the Christian community to avoid the persecution seen elsewhere. In Israel, the Christian community is actually growing. Here, I must put a slightly different slant on the issue from that of the noble lord, Lord Wright. This community has increased fourfold in the last 50 years. This largely Christian Arab community represents about 10 per cent of the total Arab population of 1.5 million within Israel proper and has tended to cluster in the mixed towns of Haifa, Nazareth and Jerusalem. They do relatively well there: there is a Christian Arab supreme court judge for example, as well as members of the Knesset and a winner of the Israeli prize for literature. They are well represented in academe and the professions. It is also the case that they have a lower infant mortality rate, lower even than that of Israeli Jews, and a higher rate of entry into higher education, especially amongst women.

Of course, they have their problems as a minority group. They have concerns about job opportunities, for example, but that has to be kept in some sort of perspective. As Andrew White, the vicar of Baghdad said 'the only place in the Middle East that Christians are really safe is Israel'. It must be responsible for the fact that Sudanese Christians were making the hazardous trek across Egypt, at risk to life and limb, to seek refuge in Israel. It can be no coincidence that the world centre for the Baha'i faith is to be found in Israel.

There are lessons in Jordan and Israel for the Middle East. Certainly a lack of benign rulers, democracy or the rule of law has not helped. Can we hope that the Arab spring will bring some improvements? The fall of ugly dictatorships must be a helpful first step but the rise of democracy alone, at least in the first instance, seems not to be enough, although I agree entirely with the noble lord, Lord Parekh, that it is much to be preferred and something that we have to foster. In Egypt, the coming to power of the Moslem Brotherhood, however transiently, was very worrying for the Christian population, and the grinding poverty so widespread there does not generally favour increased feelings of tolerance towards minorities who are often used as scapegoats.

So it would be wrong to feel much optimism for the immediate future there, although one can hope for better in the longer term. Perhaps in Tunisia there may be the possibility of better news, or more remotely in Syria or Lebanon there is some room for hope. If Assad falls, and that is a big if, there are signs that support for Hamas in Syria and for Hezbollah in Lebanon may also fall. In Lebanon at least it is largely Hezbollah that is making life difficult for the Christian community. Perhaps there is a glimmer of hope there too.

When there are such major shifts as we are now seeing across the region, there are both threats and opportunities. Let us hope and pray that the opportunities can be built upon. Meanwhile, we should offer all the support that we can to these unfortunate people.

Unfortunately, since that time there has not been any sense that conditions for the Christian communities have improved and may even have worsened.

It is difficult to escape the conclusion that the Middle East will remain in a state of turmoil for some years to come. Extremists in the different branches of Islam are maintaining a brutal war against each other and against the West and Western values. To the extent that extremists dominate and are in positions of power the future remains gloomy. For Israel, placed as it is at the epicentre of this turbulence, there are fears for its very existence. It relies heavily on its few friends in the world for support and the USA is clearly the most important of these. There is a glimmer of hope with the Russian initiative on the back of severe American-led sanctions that Iran may begin to reduce their nuclear programme. The voice of the new Iranian leader, Mr Rouhani, at the UN began to sound conciliatory even though his 'big brother' at home, the Ayatollah, was less than supportive. If Iran fails to decommission its nuclear arms programme it seems virtually inevitable that Israel will be forced to act. The results are likely to be devastating for all, both in the Middle East and elsewhere but especially for Israel. I do not envy those who have to take these impossible decisions.

Chapter 13 **Daniel**

In 2007 my life was completely upended by a tragedy that has cast a blight on everything that I have done subsequently. Nothing prepared me for Daniel's death.

I knew about death of course. As a newly qualified house officer I had watched a man die as I stood helplessly at the foot of the bed. He had had a heart attack and developed acute heart failure. Only later did I realise that in 1958 there was little I could have done. But that did not stop my feelings of remorse when I saw his look of fear as he took his last breath. Nor in later life have I managed to distance myself completely from a sense that I should have done more when I heard that one or other of my patients had died. I hasten to say that not all my patients died but in a long clinical career it was inevitable that some did and that I felt the prick of guilt when they did.

Then when my parents died the personal grief was sharp. There were tears and a deep sense of loss overlain with guilt – guilt because I was not with either of them when they passed away. But over time I adjusted even to that. Time is a great healer they say and it is, or it was, in their case.

But when Daniel died our lives were split in two – life before 16 June 2007 and life after it; reasonable contentedness before and a dark void after. I have no confidence now, six years on, that the sense of loss will ever leave me or that I will regain an easy contentment. Tears prick my eyes at some time every day. They say that pride comes before a fall. But not the sort of pride I had in Daniel nor this sort of fall.

In a dreadful twist of symmetry, he was 37 years old and I was 73, the same age as my father when he died. It is hard for me now to escape the feeling that it should have been me that died and not Daniel.

It was while on a mountain biking holiday in Malawi that he took a day off to go on a sight-seeing trip in a light aircraft. A Cessna meant for five passengers took off with an inexperienced pilot and six passengers. It flew off piste, for unknown reasons, stalled and crashed, killing all on board including two of Daniel's friends.

The way in which he died is not my concern, only the incomprehensible idea that he is dead. It is impossible even now, especially now, to get my head round this straight fact. He is always with me, but he is not.

The afternoon that the two policemen came to tell us that Daniel had been killed in an accident is sharply etched in my memory. I remember their words, how I fell on a couch and how I could not fathom what had happened to us. I looked across at stricken Edna and closed my eyes. From then on it all became very blurred. Friends suddenly surrounded us and the flat was full of quiet murmurings as we were enveloped in a sea of concern and support. Helen came from Israel. She was always very close to Daniel and was equally devastated.

The shock was almost unbearable. I stopped eating and slept only with drugs and exhaustion. Our wonderful GP suggested that perhaps an antidepressant might help but I could not see the point of trying to make me feel happy when I needed only to grieve.

The days slowly passed and life went on as it must. Eventually we were able to get out but it was a struggle physically as well as mentally.

People now say that they admire Edna and me for the way that we cope. The way, six years on, we seem to live a full life enjoying company and in good humour. But we skate on very thin ice. They do not know how near the tears are to the surface, how sharp the stabs of pain that bring us up short when we seem to be enjoying ourselves too much. They just do not know about that constant background sense of loss. It is a loss that remains incomprehensible and I do not imagine this feeling of a huge hole will ever leave us.

Of course any parent's pain at the loss of a child is barely tolerable but Daniel figured very large in our lives.

He lives in my mind in so many ways. It is difficult, for example, to understand how a shy, timid, little boy with few close friends could transform himself into a gregarious social animal. How someone seemingly so much a loner as a child could surround himself as a young adult with an army of friends with whom he was constantly in contact so that his phone never seemed to stop ringing when he was with us. He was full of fun and it was impossible to ignore his presence. And how did someone so fearful of physical sport develop such a passion for challenging activities that made my hair stand on end? Rock and ice climbing, mountain biking and triathlons were his metier. From a quiet laid-back boy he became a competitive demon on the squash court.

He drifted into a career in medicine but what a wise choice that turned out to be. He was a natural doctor. Nothing was too much as he cared for his patients and they in turn adored him. A young doctor spoke to us of his teaching skills: 'There are good teachers, there are excellent teachers and then there is Daniel'. His kindness and care for others shone through and was reflected in his ever-present grin. We, his parents, and his huge circle of friends, were constantly reminded of the warmth of his embrace.

Some of his squash-playing friends were unaware that he was even a doctor let alone a high flyer with a PhD and a prestigious lectureship. Yet he had a formidable intellect and I admired and deeply respected him for that and for the way that he did not parade it. He always seemed to get to the crux of an issue and almost instantaneously come up with a reasoned response, all without making anything of it himself. I sometimes spoke to him about a knotty issue, perhaps unrelated to medicine, an ethical matter say, and he would immediately grasp the essence of the problem and its solution while I had struggled with it for some time. I would gaze in admiration at him and he would wonder what I was making a fuss about.

James Garvill, the twentieth president of America said, in 1880:

There is nothing in all the earth that you and I can do for the dead. They are past our help and past our praise. We can add to them no glory, we can give to them no immortality. They do not need us, but forever and forever more we need them.

Daniel has left a terrible gap in our lives.

The Daniel Turnberg Middle East Travel Fellowship Scheme

The response to Daniel's death was remarkable and not simply from our and his many friends. Letters flooded in from many whom we scarcely knew as well as strangers touched by our tragedy.

Once we came out of our shock and had the strength and courage to read them we realised that many of these comforting letters had an underlying theme – a desire to see some sort of lasting commemoration of Daniel's life.

In thinking about the things Daniel himself would have liked to see we chose two in which he had a particularly keen interest. Medical research was obvious but it was his passionate interest in Israel and the Palestinians that prompted us into the scheme on which we finally decided: travel fellowships for young medical researchers in Israel and the Middle East to spend a short time in institutions in the UK.

The response when we announced our idea was overwhelming. Contributions came in thick and fast, and with the funds raised we have been able to support 121 young medical scientists during the first five years of the scheme.

The fellowship programme is fairly straightforward. It provides grants to young medical researchers from Israel, the West Bank and Gaza, Egypt, Jordan and Lebanon to spend four weeks in a British university or research institute. They come to meet experts in their field, learn new techniques and, most importantly, develop plans for continuing collaboration. In this way we have been able to encourage a remarkable number of UK–Middle East interactions that have continued well beyond the short one month of the programme.

We have met many of these young men and women, and the enthusiasm and excitement with which they told us of their experiences were heartening. Conversations with the Israelis about their research were interesting but what we did not expect was to hear that they had, without exception, been welcomed with considerable interest and a desire to hear more of Israeli affairs with no suggestion of academic boycotts or antipathy to Israel. Indeed a number of visits to Israel by UK academics followed this initial contact as well as publication of joint research papers and grant applications.

It was a pleasure too to see West Bank Palestinians engaging with UK scientists and, although contacts between Palestinian and Israeli fellows were limited, it was satisfying to hear that at this level at least there was a strong desire to see a speedy resolution of the conflict with two states living in peace. Although research collaboration between them is currently frustrated we did hear of several examples of 'unofficial' interactions and there was a clear desire to develop these further given a better political climate.

A smaller number of UK medical scientists were awarded fellowships to go to the Middle East and, at the time of writing, there were 47 Israelis, 15 Palestinians (including 2 from Gaza), 20 Egyptians, 14 Jordanians and 2 from Lebanon, with 22 from the UK going out to the Middle East, a total of 121 fellows.

We were able to support this number of fellowships because we received a generous grant from the Wellcome Trust which provided matching funding for the first five years, effectively doubling the number whom we could support. Large grants also came from the Wolfson Family Trust, the Royal College of Physicians, the Isaac and Julia Haskel Trust, the Robert Gavron Trust, GSK and many others, while the innumerable smaller grants from many friends warmed our hearts.

It was fortunate for us that the Academy of Medical Sciences took on the task of managing the programme, including the setting up of an expert scientific review panel to select applications. Their help was invaluable in narrowing down the field of candidates because we received many more potentially eligible applications than we could support.

This venture takes up some time but we continue to believe that it is providing worthwhile dividends in promoting mutual understanding and collaboration for Israel, the Middle East and the UK. It is particularly heartening to know that it is not only in the scientific arena that bonds have been forged and many personal friendships have been built. It is in these interpersonal relations that we feel we are able, in a small way, to fulfil some of Daniel's own deeply held humanitarian enthusiasms. We were very moved when one of our fellows said, 'We are all your sons now'.

Daniel lives on in other surprising ways. A bench on Hampstead Heath with an inscription dedicated to him was put up by a group of his friends. A silver chalice, the 'Daniel Turnberg Cup', is awarded each year to a young researcher at Manchester's medical school and his name has been attached to the lectureship that he occupied at the Royal Free Hospital.

But it is the mark that he left in the hearts of everyone he touched, especially his parents, that lives on.

Epilogue

At the age of 80 years I am likely to have achieved much of what I am going to do in my life, apart from crossing the 't's and dotting the 'i's. Sad thought, but true.

On occasion I have tried to get a measure of what I have managed to do. How does it match up to what I could and should have achieved? How does it match up, for example, to one of my heroes, Alf Morris, a fellow Labour peer, who died in 2012. There was a man who fought hard all his life for a cause in which he believed, that is the welfare of disabled people. It was he who successfully brought a private member's bill through the Commons to enshrine the welfare of disabled people in the law. And he never stopped. He selflessly continued to champion the needs of those he thought were disadvantaged in any of a number of ways to the end of his life. Compared with him I feel I have merely dabbled at the edges.

However, I am increasingly bolstered by the legacy I have in my children and grandchildren. I finished this tale with the loss of our son, Daniel, an event that has cast a huge shadow over my life. But when I look at my wonderful daughter, Helen, and her beautiful children, Leora, Yonah, Tsofit and David, I know how blessed I am. They are the dividends from my investment in life. My grandchildren are beautiful, clever, funny, loving and, of course, outstanding at sport, as indeed, whose grandchildren are not? Although living in Israel, soccer and cricket dominate the boys' sporting activities. It is pretty obvious to me that they do not get this fascination with sport from my side of the family and it must come from Moshe, our son-in-law. Moshe and Helen live a life of devotion, to each other, to their children and to their Judaism. It is a modern orthodox Judaism that allows them to live in the modern world while keeping to every possible observance of Jewish law and tradition. These permeate their lives and give meaning to every part of it so that they seem to be contentedly cocooned. It suits their characters perfectly as they are naturally drawn to doing good in the world, in a way that sometimes seems naïve to an old cynic like me.

But I could not have wished for a kinder, more considerate and morally upright child than Helen. She glows with an innate goodness and sense of what is right. She is perceptive, chatty, humorous and full of enthusiasm for life. I can hardly take credit for any of this because all of these characteristics, as well as her beauty, she has inherited from Edna.

The last word must go to Edna. She is the light and love of my life. I do not know how I could have survived these last few years without her constant presence by my side. When I am down, she pulls me up, when I have been ill she has been my rock and support, and when I am insufferable she simply smiles and waits for it to pass.

It was natural I suppose that she should find her niche in counselling and marriage guidance, and that has been my good fortune. It is she who has guided our marriage and made it possible for me to achieve what little I have.

I know, as was said in more than one of my school reports, I 'could do better', but I hope that my life has not been entirely in vain, and I feel that it is still possible for me to do at least a little more.

References

1 Bunker JP, Frazier HS, Mosteller F. Improving health: measuring effects of medical care. *Millbank Q* 1994;72:2258.

2 Layard R. *Happiness. Lessons from a new science*. London: Penguin Books, 2005.

3 Turnberg LA, Fordtran JS, Carter NW, Rector F Jr. Mechanisms of bicarbonate absorption and its relationship to sodium transport in the human jejunum. *J Clin Invest* 1970;49:548–56.

4 Turnberg LA, Bieberdorf EA, Morawski SG, Fordtran JS. Interrelationships of chloride, bicarbonate, sodium and hydrogen transport in human ileum. *J Clin Invest* 1970;49:557–67.

5 Black D. A Doctor Looks at Health Economics. Office of Health Economics Annual Lecture, 1994.

6 Clothier C. *The Patient's Dilemma*. The Rock Carling Fellowship, The Nuffield Provincial Hospitals Trust, 1987:4.

7 Office for National Statistics. *Mortality: 2010-based NPP reference volume*. London: ONS, 2012. www.ons.gov.uk/ons/dcp/1 (Accessed 8 February 2014).

8 Warhurst G, Higgs NB, Tonge A, Turnberg LA. Stimulatory and inhibitory actions of carbachol on chloride secretory responses in a human colonic cell line, T84. *Am J Physiol GI Liver Physiol* 1991;24:220–8.

9 Mirvis DA. Physician's autonomy – the relation between public and professional expectations. *N Engl J Med* 1993;328:1346–9.

10 Luhrman N. *Social systems*. Stamford, CA: Stamford University Press, 1995.

11 O'Neill O. *A question of trust*. Reith Lectures, 2002. Cambridge: Cambridge University Press, 2002.

12 Baroness Young. Hansard, House of Lords. Column 1105, 22 March 2012.

13 Lachmann P. *First steps: a personal account of the formation of the Academy of Medical Sciences*. London: Academy of Medical Sciences, 2010.

14 Imison C, Poteliakhoff E, Thompson J. *Older people and emergency bed use. Exploring variation*. London: King's Fund. 2012.

15 Office for National Statistics (ONS). *Interim 2011-based subnational population projections: local authorities, counties, regions and England: single years of age, persons*. London: ONS, 2012.

16 Office for National Statistics. *2010-based national population projections lifetable template: England and Wales*. London: ONS, 2011:16.

17 Filkin G, House of Lords Select Committee on Public Service and Demographic Change. *Ready for ageing? Report for Session 2012–13*. London: The Stationery Office, 2013.

18 Office for National Statistics. Pension trends. *Life expectancy and healthy Ageing*. London: ONS, 2012.

19 Davies S. Caring for the rising number of dementia patients. *Found Sci Technol J* 2012;20:16–17.

20 Roberts A, Marshall L, Charlesworth A. *A decade of austerity? The funding pressures facing the NHS from 2010/11 to 2021/22*. London: The Nuffield Trust, 2012.

21 Nuffield Trust and the PSSRU at the London School of Economics. *Care for older people – projected expenditure to 2022 on social care and continuing health care for England's older population*. London: The Nuffield Trust, 2012.

22 PSSRU at the London School of Economics. *Discussion paper 2811/2*. London: PSSRU, 2011.

23 Francis R. *Report of the Mid Staffordshire NHS Foundation Trust public inquiry*. London: The Stationery Office, 2013.

24 European Commission Eurostat. *Health statistics – Atlas on mortality in the European Union*. Luxembourg: Office for Official Publications of the European Communities, 2009.

25 Judt T. *Ill fares the land*. London: Penguin, 2010 [Excerpts from this book have been reproduced by permission of Penguin Books Ltd].

26 Timmins N. *Never again? The story of the Health and Social Care Act, 2012. A study of coalition government and policy making*. London: The King's Fund and Institute for Government, 2012.

27 Dickinson H, Glasby J. Why partnership does not work: pitfalls, problems and possibilities in English health and social care. *Public Management Rev* 2010;12:811–28.

28 Ham C. *Commissioning in the English NHS: The case for integration*. The Nuffield Trust Series Report. London: The Nuffield Trust, 2007.

29 Glasby J, Miller R. Ten years of care trusts: six key findings. *Health Serv J* 28 June 2012.

30 Jones N, Charlesworth A. *The Anatomy of Health Spending, 2011/12. Nuffield Trust review of NHS expenditure and labour productivity*. London: The Nuffield Trust, 2013.

31 Charlesworth A, Davies A, Dixon J. *Reforming payment for health care in Europe to achieve better health*. Research report for the Nuffield Trust. London: The Nuffield Trust, 2012.

32 Webster C. *The National Health Service. A political history*. Oxford: Oxford University Press, 2002: 203.

33 Glasby J, Peck E, Ham C, Dickinson H. *Things can only get better? The argument for NHS independence*. Health Services Management Centre, School of Public Health, University of Birmingham Occasional Paper. April 2007.

34 Casalino LP. *GP Commissioning in the NHS in England: Ten suggestions from the United States*. Nuffield Trust Viewpoint. London: The Nuffield Trust, June 2011.

35 Wanless D. *Securing good health for the whole population*. London: HMSO, 2004.

36 Corporate Analytical Team, Department of Health. *Explaining NHS deficits 2003/4–2005/6.* London: DH, February 2007.

37 Commonwealth Fund. *Mirror, mirror on the wall: an update on the comparative performance of American health care,* Vol. 59. Commonwealth Fund, 16 May 2007.

38 Jarman B, Gault S, Alves B *et al.* Explaining differences in English hospital death rates using routinely collected data. *BMJ* 1999;318:1515–20.

39 Jarman B. 'The quality of care in hospitals.' Harveian Oration, Royal College of Physicians, 1999.

40 Veitch K. Law, social policy and the constitution of markets and profit making. *J Law Soc* 2013;40:137–54.

41 Arora S, Charlesworth A, Kelly E, Stoye G. *Public payment and private provision. The changing landscape of health care in the 2000s.* London: Institute of Fiscal Studies and the Nuffield Trust, 2013.

42 Independent Health Care Advisory Service and the NHS Confederation Report. *What's it all for? Removing unnecessary bureaucracy in regulation.* London: The NHS Confederation and the IHAS, 2010.

43 Mandelstam M. *How we treat the sick. Neglect and abuse in our health services.* London: Jessica Kingsley, 2011.

44 Age Concern England. *Hungry to be heard: the scandal of malnourished people in hospital.* London: Age Concern, 2007.

45 Tallis R. More training won't fill a hole in humanity. *The Times* 17 February 2011.

46 Parliamentary Health Service Ombudsman. *Care and compassion? Report of the Health Service Ombudsman on ten investigations into NHS care of older people,* HC 778. London: HMSO.

47 Forder J. Long term care and hospital utilization by older people: an analysis of substitution rates. *Health Econ* 2009;18:1322–8.

48 Organisation for Economic Co-operation and Development. *OECD health data. Frequently requested data.* London: OECD, 2012.

49 Crawford R, Emmerson C. *NHS and social care funding: the outlook to 2021/22.* Research report of the Nuffield Trust and Institute of Fiscal Studies. London: The Nuffield Trust, 2012.

50 Appleby J. *Spending on health and social care over the next 50 years. Why think long term?* London: The King's Fund, 2013.

51 Layard R. *Mental health: Britain's biggest social problem.* London: London School of Economics, 2005.

52 Moussavi S, Chatterji S, Verdes E *et al.* Depression, chronic diseases and decrements in health: results from world health surveys. *Lancet* 2007;370:859–77.

53 Dilnot Commission. *Fairer care funding – the report of the Commission on Funding of Care and Support.* July 2011.

54 Department of Health. *Health services in London – a strategic review.* London: DH, 1997.

Appendices

Appendix 1 Regulatory and advisory bodies*

Care Quality Commission (from 1 April 2009)
Healthcare Commission (before 1 April 2009)
Commission for Social Care Inspection (before 1 April 2009)
Mental Health Act Commission
Monitor
Audit Commission
National Audit Office
NHS Litigation Authority
National Patient Safety Agency
Connecting for Health Information Governance toolkit
NHS Estates – cleaning
Postgraduate Medical Education and Training Board (subsequently Health Education England)
Clinical Pathology Accreditation Limited
British Association for Counselling and Psychotherapy
Investors in People
Royal colleges (13)
National Treatment Agency for Substance Misuse
Quality in Drugs and Alcohol Services
Quality Network CAMHS (Child and Adolescent Mental Health Services)
Quality Inpatient CAMHS
Standards for Health Promotion in Hospitals
Service Standards for Addiction Therapeutic Communities

*From the Independent Healthcare Advisory Service and the NHS Confederation Report: *What is it all for? Removing unnecessary bureaucracy in regulation.* London: The NHS Confederation and the IHAS, 2010.[42]

Appendix 2 **Care of the elderly: a quiet disgrace**

Lords debate, 31 March 2011

That the service for some groups of patients is far from perfect is emphasised every week by reports of neglect of the elderly in hospitals and care homes and by inadequate care for the mentally ill. I initiated a debate on care of the elderly on 31 March 2011, in the House of Lords. I said:

> *As someone who has spent most of his life working in the National Health Service I bow to no one in my support and admiration of what it achieves. I see enormous advances being made every year, and patients who would no doubt have died are now cured and survive into old age. Medicine has been transformed out of all recognition during my working life.*
>
> *It is because I have this pride and huge admiration for the NHS and the people who work in it that I now feel a deep sense of shame. Despite these wonderful advances, in too many places we have been ignoring the common decency needed to care for the vulnerable, the sick and the elderly and it is the elderly who are often the most vulnerable. As Ann Abraham, the health service ombudsman, said in her report there is a, 'gulf between the principles and values of the NHS Constitution and the felt reality of being an older person in the care of the NHS in England'.*
>
> *That is why I am going to focus on the elderly, but they are not the only group where standards have slipped. I suspect that other noble Lords may speak about the mentally ill, and only the other day we had a report about failures in maternity services. Of course, the media are quick to pick up the seemingly occasional horror stories of neglect in a hospital. You might want to hide behind the idea that these are rare incidents against a background in which 1 million people are looked after perfectly well in our hospitals and nursing homes every 36 hours, and that is absolutely true. But it turns out that it is not so rare or unusual an event and it seems to be happening far too often. Stories of neglect are just too common for comfort: patients, usually in a geriatric ward, unable to eat the food left out of reach at the end of the bed and collected by staff seemingly unaware that it has not been touched, and too busy to notice that a thirsty patient is unable to even drink without help or, worse, too busy to notice that a helpless patient, unable to get out of bed and incontinent, is sitting in damp sheets for hours or, the final degradation, soiled by faeces and unwashed for days.*

Noble Lords may ask whether I exaggerate. Where is the evidence that this picture is not just a rare, occasional lapse in an otherwise acceptable system of care? Well, quite apart from the rather common anecdotes of many with elderly relatives, there is now the report of the ombudsman in which she describes 10 examples of the complaints she receives that emphasise just how bad it can get.

We cannot say that we have not been warned. In 1997 we had the report from Age Concern in its 'Dignity on the Ward' campaign, describing failing standards of care. When it followed that up 10 years later, in 2007, it found that little or nothing had changed. The Commission for Health Improvement in 2003, the Healthcare Commission in 2007 and the Care Quality Commission in 2010, despite regularly changing their names, came up with the same message. Now there is the book that has just been published, Michael Mandelstam's How we treat the sick, *that brings all this together in a devastating way.*

The scandal at the mid-Staffordshire hospital of a year or so ago turns out not to be an isolated example. Every time we have a disastrous fall in standards we have another report or enquiry. I will not list all the hospitals or nursing homes that have been the subject of criticism but they range from Cornwall to Rotherham, from Thameside to Southampton and from Oxford to Bolton. There are just too many, and it is clearly not a new phenomenon. It went on under the past government and the one before that, so I do not want to make any political points here. But how can we have tolerated this neglect of our most vulnerable citizens for so long?

No one can afford to be sanguine: not the doctors, not the nurses, not the managers and not the government. I want to say a few words about why and how this is happening and suggest what we might do about it, because we certainly cannot allow it to go on.

Let me apologise for starting with the nurses, for whom I have the greatest admiration and to whom I owe a great deal of personal gratitude. However, at the end of the day it is to the nurses that patients look first for their personal care and empathy. It is always tempting to look back to a golden age that never was, but one thing that is clearly fixed in my mind is how high the standards of nursing care were on the medical wards where I worked in the 1950s and the 1960s. Those were the days when the sister in charge of her ward really was in charge. She was usually a mature woman in a career job who made absolutely certain that everything ran efficiently and well. I admit to running scared of her, as indeed did the patients.

However, those were the days before the revolutions in nurse management and nurse education. One of the consequences of the upward drive to better-educated nurses with university degrees has been the development of a generation whose aspirations are set high. They quite reasonably expect to have a career in which they can practise their skills to a high standard. Who can blame them? They do a great job with all the caring attitudes you could wish for. However, that has left a gap at the more basic and, to many, less attractive level of the general and geriatric ward where there is a greater emphasis on the basic needs of patients: feeding, washing, help with movement, going to the toilet and so on.

Those are the wards where staffing levels are often lower per patient in the belief that they do not need the more intensive, one-to-one care of the specialist units. So they are often understaffed and sometimes come to rely on temporary, or 'bank', staff who constantly change. Continuity of care is damaged as patients, already a little disorientated by being removed from their familiar environment, are faced with a bewildering series of new faces.

It is not only the nurses who are constantly changing. Confusion is compounded by the way the rotas for the ward doctors are arranged to fit in with the European Working Time

Directive or as they rotate through yet another experience to chalk up on their training programme. So there are new faces at every turn.

These wards do not have the champions that the specialised departments have, who can put pressure on management to protect them from cuts. Not much wonder that nurses in training pass through these experiences quickly on their way to higher things. Nursing sisters in charge may not stay long enough to be able to stamp their authority and, in any case, are distracted by paperwork or nowadays feeding data into their computers – care plans and the like.

I fear that these changes have created a situation in which we have two starkly different standards of care. On the one hand, we have highly trained, highly professional and caring nurses in well-staffed, specialised units – intensive care, coronary care, chemotherapy units and the like – and, on the other hand, poorly staffed wards, rushed nurses, falling morale, falling standards and poor supervision. These are the staff who are struggling to cope with patients whose vulnerability makes enormous demands for the care and attention that the nurses have neither the time nor the patience for.

Of course, this picture is not true everywhere and many, probably most, wards and hospitals are very good indeed. It is just that this picture is too common for us to take any comfort from it.

So what is to be done? Here it is clear that there is a need for a multi-focused set of actions which no one profession or body can shirk. First, we must have someone at ward level who takes full responsibility for ensuring that patients are properly looked after with the respect and dignity that they deserve. That is absolutely key. I hope that my nursing friends will forgive me for saying that we should be making this job, the ward sister or charge nurse, a career post and rewarding those who do it accordingly. There has to be some continuity in the post to make it an attractive alternative to the lofty pastures of the specialised departments.

Then there is the issue of too few carers on the wards. What happened to all those state-enrolled nurses – the SENs – whose roles were predominantly in the caring world and who did not aspire to higher degrees? They disappeared in Project 2000. Is it possible for us to resurrect the SEN grade and make it attractive again? I hope that some thought can be given to that.

That leads me to the medical profession, who cannot absolve themselves – ourselves – from responsibility for the neglect we are now discussing. They, after all, must see the way their patients are being cared for and, I'm afraid, have not raised their voices loud enough. They should be leading the charge for proper staffing levels on their wards. They should be pressing hard on the managers of their hospitals. And they really must do something about these disruptive rotas that are destroying the continuity of care that patients need and deserve.

The managers must make themselves more aware of their responsibility to ensure that there are sufficient staff on these wards to cope with what is one of the most demanding areas of the hospital. They should know that these wards cannot be among the first to take cuts. Then there are the responsibilities of the trust boards. Board members have to be rather more hands on and need to know what is going on in their wards. Many obviously do, but it seems that there are too many who do not.

Finally, I come to those bodies who will be commissioning services in the bright new tomorrow, the GP commissioning groups (later changed to clinical commissioning groups [CCGs]) and the responsibilities that we should be placing on them for standards of care in the NHS, under the Health and Social Care Bill coming through this house – in whatever *form that bill survives. To paraphrase Aneurin Bevan, there are bedpans clanging on the floor all over the country and, in the rush to devolution to the local level, important though that is, devolved responsibility must also mean some central accountability.*

As these services are commissioned, we must make sure that the Bill places a duty on the CCGs so that high standards of care for the elderly are a contractual obligation on the providers. Furthermore, we must have a robust system of monitoring so that we can have some confidence that this care is actually being provided. Perhaps the proposed Commissioning Board can take this on, but only if it has the capacity to monitor what is going on in hospitals and nursing homes, and has a mechanism for action when standard slips.

We have been through too many years in which we have seen indifference punctuated by intermittent reports and wringing of hands. It has to stop. The time for action is now.

Eighteen months on and it is not at all clear that there has been much change. I led another debate on 'Care of the elderly in the community' in March 2013 in which I entered the battlefield again. This time I had the vain hope of persuading the government to redirect resources from such ventures as nuclear submarines and high-speed trains to care in the community. I pointed to the need to consider where our priorities should lie and to the likelihood that the public at large might give the way we care for our elderly people a higher priority than a number of other objectives. I doubt if I have persuaded ministers of the wisdom, as I see it, of such a proposal.

We now have a remarkable health service, mostly fit for the purpose of caring for acute illnesses, in the community or in hospital, and for the services provided by general practitioners whose standards are high in many places. But there are large gaps in the provision of long-term care for elderly people, at home and in the community as well as in hospital, and for mentally ill individuals. It is here that we should be focusing much more attention. In doing so it will be no good simply suggesting that elderly patients should not be cared for long term in hospital, true though that may be. But if the services in the community, in care homes, or the support needed to keep them at home is not available, there may be little choice. We should first invest in those facilities as I have described, so that transfer from hospital can be rapidly and easily arranged. It is then that we might be able to reduce hospital beds to the number required to meet the acute and specialised needs of the population, but not before. Answer the question first about where patients will go before trying to offer a solution to bed numbers.